WELCOME...

Stephen Fry has a lot to answer for. I'm an avid viewer of his TV panel show *QI*, but as a result of watching it I found I knew less than I did before. Things I thought I knew turned out to be urban myths, or solid facts that simply weren't true. Every time I heard the hooting of the QI klaxon, another of life's certainties evaporated into thin air.

Luckily, I had something to fall back on – a way of rebuilding my brain's storehouse of knowledge. It's the Q&A section you'll find in every issue of *BBC Focus* magazine. All the questions are sent in by readers and answered by our panel of experts. And since *BBC Focus* is a science and technology magazine, the questions cover pretty much anything you might want to know about the world.

I've certainly learned a lot from reading the Q&A section over the years. I've also learned that *BBC Focus* is always attracting new readers, because some of the questions we receive have been answered before. That's why, a couple of years ago, we decided to publish a compendium of the most interesting Q&As in a special issue. The fact that it sold out was a pleasant surprise. But rather than reprinting it, we decided to wait until we could gather a few more nuggets of knowledge.

You're now reading the second volume, which includes questions like: do dogs have a better memory than cats (p17)?; why do we have earlobes (p24)?; and where does water come from (p93)? If nothing else, I'm now a little better prepared for the next series of *QI*...

Graham Southorn, Editor

THE EXPERTS

SUSAN BLACKMORE
Susan is a visiting psychology professor at the University of Plymouth. Her books include *The Meme Machine*

DR ALASTAIR GUNN
Alastair is a radio astronomer at the Jodrell Bank Centre for Astrophysics at the University of Manchester

ROBERT MATTHEWS
After studying physics at Oxford, Robert became a science writer. He's a visiting reader in science at Aston University

GARETH MITCHELL
Starting out as a broadcast engineer, Gareth now writes and presents *Click* on the BBC World Service

LUIS VILLAZON
Luis has a BSc in computing and an MSc in zoology from Oxford. His works include *How Cows Reach The Ground*

Editorial
Editor Graham Southorn
Managing Editor Nige Tassell
Production Editor Rebecca Candler
Editorial Assistant Emma Jolliffe

Art & Pictures
Art Editor Lisa White
Picture Editors James Cutmore, Rhiannon Furbear-Williams

Press and Public Relations
Press Officer Carolyn Wray
0117 314 8812
carolyn.wray@immediate.co.uk

Production
Production Director Sarah Powell
Production Co-ordinator Emily Mounter
Reprographics Tony Hunt, Chris Sutch

Circulation / Advertising
Circulation Manager Rob Brock

Publishing
Publisher Andrew Davies
Publishing Director Andy Healy
Managing Director Andy Marshall
Chairman Stephen Alexander
Deputy Chairman Peter Phippen
CEO Tom Bureau
Like what you've read? Email us at **bookazines@immediate.co.uk**

CONTENTS

THE BIG PICTURE

Do sea urchins poo?

Yes, you're staring at its bottom! After munching on bacteria, seaweed and other food with the mouth on its underside, the urchin converts waste into round pellets, which are pushed out through a transparent anal tube at the top. "These animals have this tube so they can eject faeces away from their bodies, so they're not pooping all over themselves," says Dr Dave Pawson, curator of echinoderms at the Smithsonian Institution in Washington DC.

Like most echinoderms, urchins have five-sided radial symmetry. The five parts are easy to see in this shallow-water species, *Astropyga radiata*, thanks to its bright blue spots, known as iridophores. Members of this species are also known as 'fire urchins' because, although they're not venomous, divers pierced by their long spines experience a burning bacterial infection.

DAVID FLEETHAM/NATUREPL.COM

Is this proof of life on another planet?

Not quite. This may look like a settlement on Europa, an icy moon orbiting Jupiter, but this futuristic building is actually much closer to home, in the Antarctic.

Halley VI is a science research centre run by the British Antarctic Survey (BAS) at the bottom of Earth. It's a string of eight modules, each of which can be relocated by towing it across the ice on skis. This is a vital feature because the station sits on the Brunt Ice Shelf, which is flowing into the sea at a rate of 400m per year. What's more, each module has hydraulic legs so the station can be raised above the snowdrifts that buried its predecessors. "The module you see in the foreground has an observation deck," says Dr Anna Jones, a BAS atmospheric chemist. "Inside there's a spectrophotometer that takes measurements of the ozone layer – it's similar to the instrument that enabled Halley scientists to discover the ozone hole in the 1980s. Our long-term measurements are crucial for understanding how Antarctica's atmosphere and climate are changing."

BRITISH ANTARCTIC SURVEY

SAM DOBSON/CATERS NEWS

Why is this water red and icy?

This photograph may look like a scene from an exotic exoplanet, but it's actually the edge of a small lake in the Rhône delta in southern France.

The white substance seen clinging to the shoreline and to the twigs is not ice but common salt, which has evaporated out of the lagoon's incredibly salty water. The water appears red as an indirect result of its extreme saltiness: the colouration is caused by the high levels of halophilic – or salt-loving – microorganisms that live within it. Similar colouration can be seen in other salt-saturated waters around the world, such as Great Salt Lake in Utah.

"The colour of such hypersaline brines is in part caused by the unicellular alga *Dunaliella salina*, which is high in beta carotene," says Professor Aharon Oren of the Hebrew University of Jerusalem. "Other organisms can also be involved, such as a bacterium named *Salinibacter ruber*. They have a high concentration of carotenoid pigments in their cell membrane, which helps protect them from UV radiation."

For more great pictures, follow us on http://pinterest.com/sciencefocus

ANIMAL KINGDOM

From dinosaur eggs to deceiving butterflies, the animal world has evolved in some mysterious ways to give creatures extraordinary and unique traits

WHAT'S THE NOISIEST ANIMAL IN THE WORLD?

That depends what you mean by noisiest. But if you mean loudest, then the Smithsonian National Zoo in the USA reckons that the blue whale's low-frequency pulses win. At up to 188 decibels (dB), they are louder than a jet engine and can be detected over 500 miles away. On land, the loudest animals are probably howler monkeys (pictured), which can be heard three miles away. The loudest amphibian, at 100dB, is the common coqui frog native to Puerto Rico.

Similarly loud among birds are oil birds, which, like bats, live in caves and use echolocation. Their clicks and squawks can reach 100db and thousands of them nest together. One species of water boatman, the size of a grain of rice, can 'sing' at 103dB by rubbing his penis against his belly in a process similar to how crickets chirp. This is the loudest known sound relative to the size of the animal.

ALAMY X2, THINKSTOCK X2

DO ANIMALS EVER LIE?

Not exactly, but many animals deceive each other. A butterfly with large eye-spots on its wings appears much larger and more dangerous than it is, while a stick insect 'pretends' to be an inedible twig. These kinds of deception are hard-wired, as are some behaviours, such as when ground-nesting birds lure predators away from chicks in their nest by feigning a broken wing.

Closer to lying are the deceptive behaviours of many primates. Monkeys and baboons will distract the attention of others to snatch food, or wait until fights break out to grab a chance to mate. Chimpanzees are even more devious and in experiments have been shown to take circuitous routes to get to food so that the observers can't see them. Real deception like this requires considerable intelligence, possibly including the ability to imagine what another animal is seeing or thinking. One theory is that human intelligence evolved from our ability to deceive others.

DID YOU KNOW?

The blue whale has the largest heart of any animal. Rather incredibly, it's roughly the size of a Volkswagen Beetle.

WHY DON'T BIRDS FREEZE IN WINTER?

Lots of birds do freeze in winter. But natural selection operates quite ruthlessly against this premature end - any that freeze to death before they have raised offspring are eliminated from the gene pool. Birds have therefore evolved a variety of strategies to avoid this fate.

Like mammals, birds are warm-blooded and well-insulated, so provided they can find enough food, they can stay warm. Pigeons and crows are opportunistic scavengers, for whom towns and cities provide extra sources of food. Very small birds, like the wren, will build nests that are fully enclosed and may even nest together in groups to conserve heat. And, of course, lots of birds migrate. Many of the birds we see in Britain during winter have actually migrated from even colder countries - the Russian robin, for example, is a regular winter visitor.

DO ANIMALS SWEAT?

Some do, some don't. Many mammals, including most primates, sweat to regulate their temperature when too hot, but few do so as much as humans and horses. Even though we use the expression 'sweat like a pig', pigs have very few functional sweat glands, which is why they like to roll in water or mud when they are too hot.

Bears have sweat glands, but dogs have very few and instead cool themselves by panting, which evaporates water from the mouth and tongue. Cats sweat through their paws and also cool themselves by washing.

Birds also lack sweat glands and stay cool by panting, raising their feathers and cooling from their legs and feet. Reptiles and insects have no need to sweat because, unlike mammals, they don't need to maintain a constant body temperature.

WERE DINOSAUR EGGS THE SAME SHAPE AS BIRD EGGS?

The basic constraint on the shape of an egg is that it must fit through the pelvic canal. The shell is still somewhat pliable when it is laid, and the squeezing from the pelvic muscles tends to form an ovoid (the word comes from the Latin for 'egg') with a tapering rear end. Birds with large clutch sizes tend to have more rounded eggs because these pack better within the oviduct - the passage leading from the ovaries to the vagina - and stay warmer in the nest. Birds that nest on cliff ledges, like the guillemot, have pointier eggs that roll in a tight circle. Dinosaurs nested on the ground, so their eggs were more symmetrical. But they were also more elongated because this allows for a larger embryo, while still allowing the egg to fit through a narrow opening.

CAN SHARKS LIVE IN FRESHWATER RIVERS?

Most can't, but there are five shark species in the genus Glyphis that have adapted to live in the rivers of India and southeast Asia. The bull shark is able to move between saltwater and freshwater by adjusting the concentrations of urea and trimethylamine oxide in its blood. It takes a few days to make the change as the shark moves up or down the estuary.

CAN ANIMALS BE RIGHT- OR LEFT-HANDED?

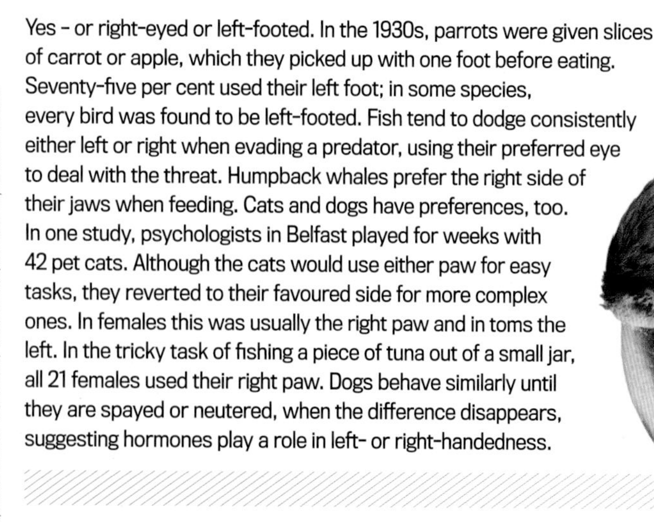

Yes - or right-eyed or left-footed. In the 1930s, parrots were given slices of carrot or apple, which they picked up with one foot before eating. Seventy-five per cent used their left foot; in some species, every bird was found to be left-footed. Fish tend to dodge consistently either left or right when evading a predator, using their preferred eye to deal with the threat. Humpback whales prefer the right side of their jaws when feeding. Cats and dogs have preferences, too. In one study, psychologists in Belfast played for weeks with 42 pet cats. Although the cats would use either paw for easy tasks, they reverted to their favoured side for more complex ones. In females this was usually the right paw and in toms the left. In the tricky task of fishing a piece of tuna out of a small jar, all 21 females used their right paw. Dogs behave similarly until they are spayed or neutered, when the difference disappears, suggesting hormones play a role in left- or right-handedness.

CORBIS/LOUIE PSIHOYOS, ALAMY, THINKSTOCK, NATURE PL/JURGEN FREUND

WHY DO SOME FISH SWIM IN SCHOOLS AND OTHERS ALONE?

Schooling is a tactic that has several advantages. It reduces vulnerability to predators, improves access to breeding partners and lowers the hydrodynamic drag when swimming at speed. It can also make it easier to find food, but not under all circumstances, and this is the primary reason that some fish do not school.

When a fish feeds on large numbers of highly mobile prey much smaller than itself, swimming in a school makes hunting easier. This is because prey that jumps out of the way of a neighbour's mouth might land itself within striking distance. But if the food source is solitary or well hidden, or if the fish feeds on plants, then other fish just represent more competition for a limited resource, making it better off feeding alone.

DO ANIMALS SEE COLOUR THE WAY WE DO?

No. Every species has a different visual system depending on the conditions under which it evolved and what their ancestors needed to see. Colour vision can be investigated by training animals to find a reward associated with one colour rather than another; only if they can see the difference can they learn the task. From such experiments we know that most mammals have limited colour vision and are usually red-green colour blind, including dogs, cats and most farm animals. Some monkeys and all apes have vision similar to ours; they are trichromats, meaning that they have three types of cone (the colour receptors in the eye). Many other mammals are dichromats, but nocturnal mammals have little or no colour vision.

In the rest of the animal world, colour vision is more bizarre. Many birds, fish, reptiles and amphibians, as well as some invertebrates, have more than three cone types, meaning they can distinguish far more colours than we can. Many insects have rich colour vision. Bees are trichromats, but while they can't see red, they can see ultraviolet, which we can't. The most complex colour vision systems are found in crustaceans, such as the mantis shrimp, which is thought to have 12 different receptor types. It is impossible for us humans, with just three, even to imagine the colours it sees.

DO ANIMALS PERCEIVE TIME?

All but the simplest animals will change their behaviour based on things that have happened to them in the past and they are sensitive to the time of day and the season. But that's not the same thing as an episodic sense of time - that is, the ability to remember specific events from their personal past. Research with rats, pigeons and apes has shown that animals can remember how long ago an event occurred, but not when. It's as if they are simply tracking the strength of a fading memory, rather than placing it on an internal calendar.

Part of the reason for this may be that an autobiographical sense of the past depends on having sufficient language and number skills to create a calendar as a framework. Research has shown that even humans don't have much of an episodic memory before the age of four. Another possibility may be that their 'time horizon' is simply much nearer than ours. Rats have been shown to anticipate rewards no more than 30 minutes into the future. With monkeys, if you give them a choice between two bananas or one, they choose two. But ask them to choose between five bananas and 10, and they don't care. Tomorrow they will be hungry again, but this future self doesn't seem to exist in their minds.

ALAMY X3, GETTY IMAGES

DO DOGS HAVE BETTER MEMORIES THAN CATS?

They have different kinds of memory, so it's hard to say which is better. Dogs are easier to train than cats, but this may be because they evolved to hunt in packs, cooperate with other dogs and be subservient to a leader. Their memory requires plenty of reinforcement, otherwise they quickly forget. But they can be rewarded, as can children, simply by giving them attention.

Cats evolved to hunt solo and are much more devious. They too can be trained, but do not have the dog's desire to please - and they need direct rewards, such as food. But both species have excellent memory for people and places, enabling them to build complex mental maps of their surroundings and to find their way home.

HOW DO ANIMALS KNOW WHERE TO MIGRATE?

Some birds, fish, turtles and whales travel enormous distances when migrating, to find food or to mate. The furthest may be the bar-tailed godwit, flying over 10,000km from New Zealand to Alaska. Starlings use a Sun compass, which means knowing the time so as to compensate for the Sun's changing position. By contrast, mallards can find north using the stars, an ability that is genetically programmed.

Many other birds, as well as salamanders, salmon and hamsters, use the earth's magnetic field. Loggerhead turtles can even sense the direction and strength of Earth's magnetic field soon after hatching and later use this skill to navigate along their regular migration route.

Other animals use land features, such as mountain ranges and rivers, and dolphins use the shape of the ocean floor. Wildebeest follow the scent of rain, while salmon use smell to return to the very same stream that they were born in.

200

The number of consecutive days that three swifts were found to have stayed aloft, without stopping for a rest, during and after their migration from Europe to North Africa.

TOP TEN

LONGEST LAND MAMMAL PREGNANCIES

1. Elephant
Duration: 21-22 months
Maximum birth weight: 120kg
Life span: Up to 80 years

2. Rhinoceros
Duration: 16-18 months
Maximum birth weight: 65kg
Life span: Up to 50 years

3. Giraffe
Duration: 15 months
Maximum birth weight: 75kg
Life span: Up to 25 years

4. Camel
Duration: 13-14 months
Maximum birth weight: 50kg
Life span: Up to 50 years

5. Tapir
Duration: 13 months
Maximum birth weight: 10kg
Life span: Up to 30 years

6. Donkey
Duration: 12 months
Maximum birth weight: 25kg
Life span: Up to 50 years

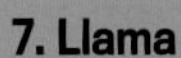

7. Llama
Duration: 11-12 months
Maximum birth weight: 14kg
Life span: Up to 25 years

8. Horse
Duration: 11 months
Maximum birth weight: 55kg
Life span: Up to 60 years

9. Cow
Duration: 11 months
Maximum birth weight: 55kg
Life span: Up to 60 years

10. Human
Duration: 9 months
Maximum birth weight: 7kg
Life span: Up to 123 years

ALAMY X4, THINKSTOCK X6

DO ANIMALS GET HAYFEVER?

We are animals and some of us get it, so the answer is yes. But if you mean other species, then some do show allergic reactions to grass and tree pollen. Most animals have no problems. After all, they have evolved and lived their lives along with pollen-producing plants. The worst cases are pet dogs and cats, who may have lost their natural immunity either through selective breeding or from being kept mostly indoors in pollen-free air and then let outside. Some symptoms are similar to those of humans, including itchy skin and ears, and watery eyes. Even herds of domestic cattle have been known to show signs of pollen allergy.

HOW CAN CROCODILES SURVIVE SO LONG WITHOUT EATING?

Crocodiles have a very slow metabolism and are cold-blooded, with tiny brains that don't need to be kept warm. So unlike mammals such as ourselves, they don't need to use a lot of energy maintaining a constant body temperature. They are ectotherms, which means that they get heat from their environment, basking in the Sun when they need to warm up and get moving, or cooling off in water. They can also slow their heartbeat to one or two beats per minute.

Crocodiles have extremely acidic stomachs that enable them to digest bones, shells and even horns to extract as much energy as possible from their prey. And when they've had a good meal, they can store a high proportion of the energy it contains. Although most crocodiles eat about 50 meals a year, they can survive a whole year, and sometimes even two or three years, without eating anything.

WHY DO BIRDS NEVER CRASH INTO EACH OTHER WHEN FLYING IN GROUPS?

Many large birds, such as geese and pelicans, fly in a V-formation, or echelon, both to improve flight efficiency and to avoid collisions. Drag is reduced by as much as 65 per cent, while range can be increased by over 70 per cent because each bird flies in the upwash from the wing tip vortex of the one in front and uses its updraft. Only the leading bird fails to benefit, but the other birds in the flock shift around in the group to share the burden. In fact, echelons are rarely perfect Vs and more often are J shapes. In either shape, each bird gets the best possible view of the bird in front so that it can maintain a safe distance and so avoid collisions.

Smaller birds gain less advantage from flying in these shapes and fly in looser groups. When we watch them, it seems miraculous that they don't collide, but their visual system works much faster than ours, just as their metabolism and muscles do. Speeded-up films of people walking in crowded streets can appear just as miraculous.

WHY DO MOTHS FLY TOWARDS THE LIGHT?

Moths are 'positively phototactic', meaning that they move towards light. Some migrating moths use the Moon to navigate and can calibrate their flight paths as it moves across the sky. This is called 'transverse orientation'. So if their instinct is to keep the Moon at a certain angle, then mistaking a light bulb for the Moon might easily get them circling around. But many moths don't migrate.

Another theory suggests that female pheromones glow faintly and emit infrared at the same frequency as candles. So male moths might go to their fiery deaths trying to mate with a candle. However, UV also attracts insects more than infrared, and electric light differs from candles, so there is no simple answer to this one.

WHY DOES A TORTOISE LIVE FOR SO LONG?

Tortoises are only at significant risk of predation for the first few years of their life. After that, their hard shell - and the fact that they spend most of the day in their burrow - keeps them safe. Tortoises can endure long periods of drought and also have very slow metabolisms. Most live for 70 years, but the record is 188 years.

WHY DO STARLINGS FLOCK TOGETHER AT DUSK?

For protection in numbers – and to keep warm when roosting for the night. These huge, wheeling, chattering dark clouds of starlings are known as 'murmurations' and form in the evening as the birds return from foraging as far as 32km away.

In the UK, the autumn murmurations begin around November, with the flocks growing larger as migrant birds from continental Europe arrive for the winter. Although most number between 5,000 and 50,000 birds, one Yorkshire murmuration used to boast 1.5 million. By flocking in such large numbers, the birds are safer from sparrowhawks and peregrine falcons that try to pick out a meal from the fast-moving crowd.

Each bird tries to fly as close as possible to its neighbours and avoid being caught on the outside of the flock. It is this simple behaviour that creates the spectacular patterns we see in the sky.

WHY DO EARTHWORMS SURFACE AFTER THE RAIN?

People often claim that avoiding being drowned is the explanation, yet earthworms breathe by exchanging oxygen and carbon dioxide through their skin, which they keep wet with a slimy mucus. This means they are happiest in damp soil and most species can survive for several days under water. So a brief rainstorm should not bother them. Indeed, they may even exploit the wet weather to travel longer distances than they would normally be able to underground.

Some may need to come to the surface to mate when it is wet enough, but only a very few of the 4,400 known species of earthworms do this. Another possibility is that earthworms confuse the sound of rain with a predator, such as a mole, and so make their way upwards to the surface to escape. Certainly the animals are well known to respond to such sounds, as any worm catcher will tell you. Some old tricks include vibrating sticks, saws on wooden stakes and, more bizarrely, giving worms tea and beer.

GETTY IMAGES X2, THINKSTOCK X2, ALAMY

WHY DO BEES BUZZ?

Bees and other Neoptera insects don't flap their wings directly. Instead, the flight muscles pull on the springy thorax wall to make it 'ping' in and out. Bees also have muscles that can contract multiple times from a single nerve impulse. Together these adaptations allow bees to beat their wings at 200-230Hz (cycles per second). We hear this as a buzzing tone. Bees also buzz when not flying, in order to shake pollen from a flower onto their body.

CAN DOGS LAUGH?

Dogs make a sort of breathy, panting sound when they are playing. If you record this and play it back to other dogs, it appears to reduce their stress behaviours, such as barking and pacing, and increase their social behaviours, such as lip licking. Is that the same thing as laughter? Or is it just the dog equivalent of a broad smile? It's hard to say. Humans mostly laugh at verbal jokes and seeing other people fall over, neither of which have much effect on dogs.

HOW MUCH WEIGHT CAN AN ANT CARRY?

At least half a gramme – which doesn't sound much, until you realise it's around 100 times an ant's weight. But we shouldn't feel too embarrassed about being out-lifted by an insect. Indeed, paradoxically it's because ants are so tiny that they have such impressive strength relative to their weight.

To see this, imagine an ant scaled up to be as large as a human. It would be around 300 times longer, while its increased volume would make its body weight around 10 million times greater. However, the strength of the ant's muscles depends on the number of fibres they contain, and thus on their cross-sectional area. So the 300x larger ant would have muscles only around 100,000 times stronger. The human-sized ant may be much heftier, but its muscle strength hasn't increased to compensate and it can barely lift its own body weight – just like us.

PHOTO COURTESY OF LAWRENCE BERKELEY NAT'L LAB

Is this a scene from a sci-fi movie?

No, this is real! Deep beneath a mountain in China, these golden orbs are detecting antineutrinos. These subatomic particles, the antimatter version of neutrinos, are produced during nuclear reactions (for instance, in the Sun) and hardly interact with matter. They come in three 'flavours' - electron, muon and tau antineutrinos - and can shift from one form to another.

The picture shows one of the eight antineutrino detectors that make up the Daya Bay Reactor Neutrino Experiment Facility. At the core of each detector is a clear acrylic chamber filled with a liquid that emits light when hit by antineutrinos. These flashes are picked up by the orbs.

The experiment studies electron antineutrinos from two nuclear reactors near Hong Kong. By comparing the number detected close to the reactors with those found further away, physicists are learning more about the transition of electron antineutrinos to other types.

For more great pictures, follow us on http://pinterest.com/sciencefocus

HUMAN BODY

Humans have evolved into well-oiled machines, but how our body parts function as they do remains intriguing

WHY DO WE HAVE EARLOBES?

Earlobes have a good blood supply and may help keep the ear warm. But it could be that natural selection simply hasn't eliminated them yet. There is also some evidence that we find earlobes attractive and therefore favour them when choosing partners.

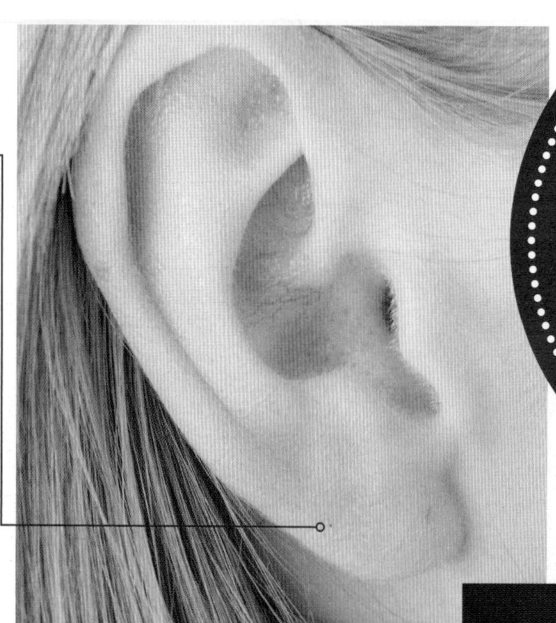

DID YOU KNOW?

Tsutomu Yamaguchi survived two nuclear bombs. In 1945, he escaped Hiroshima with burns and was bombed three days later in Nagasaki.

WHY DO HUMANS CRY?

Either for emotional reasons, or to wash away irritants such as dust, grit, insects and 'lachrymatory agents' - chemicals that make you cry. When an onion is cut, its enzymes mix with sulphoxides and sulphenic acids to produce a gas called propanethiol S-oxide, which reacts with tears to form sulphuric acid. This irritation alerts brain systems that then tell the lacrimal glands to stimulate tears to wash it away. These are called 'reflex tears' and are also provoked by coughing and yawning.

Emotional tears are different, containing more prolactin, adrenocorticotropic hormone and encephalin (a natural painkiller). Parts of the brain's limbic system, including the hypothalamus, control emotional responses including fear, anger and grief, and can signal the lacrimal glands to produce tears.

The really difficult question is why emotional humans cry at all. The reason may be social. Blurred vision and sobbing provide a social signal of weakness and neediness, and crying can bring groups together - for example, when a family is in a state of grief.

WHY DO WOMEN NEED FEWER CALORIES THAN MEN?

Only about 20 per cent of the calories you need every day are used by your physical exertion. Another 10 per cent goes into keeping your body warm, but the remaining 70 per cent is consumed by the basic cellular processes of life - a lot of it is just used to regulate the osmotic balance of each cell.

Men tend to be heavier than women, and taller too, so their internal organs and muscles are all larger. Women also have a slightly higher proportion of body fat, which requires very little energy to sustain it. Together, these two factors mean that men require about 500 extra calories each day.

WHAT ACTUALLY HAPPENS WHEN YOUR LEG 'GOES TO SLEEP'?

The temporary numbness is called paraesthesia and is caused by pressure on the *vasa nervorum*, the small arteries that supply oxygen and nutrients to the peripheral nerves of the body. When these arteries are squeezed, the nerves become partially starved of oxygen. Blood pressure behind the blockage also rises and this causes fluid to leak from the blood vessels and squeeze the nerves themselves. As the nerves stop firing, sensory signals from the skin don't reach the brain, so your leg feels numb, and motor impulse signals are unable to reach the muscles, so your leg becomes floppy and unresponsive.

Once the pressure is removed, blood starts to flow again but different nerves recover at different rates. So you feel the hot flush as the temperature-sensitive nerves reactivate, before your motor nerves allow you to move the foot. Finally, the sensory nerves in the skin begin firing wildly, which gives the pins-and-needles sensation.

CAN THE HUMAN VOICE REACH A PITCH THAT'S INAUDIBLE TO THE HUMAN EAR?

No. The maximum human vocal range runs from 60-7,000Hz, comfortably inside the normal hearing range of 20-20,000Hz. The reason we have evolved ears with a wider range than our voice is to help locate the direction a sound is coming from. A sound coming from one side of you will have a different frequency profile at your right and left ear, because your head absorbs some frequencies better than others. The effect is most pronounced at very high frequencies, so we have evolved high-frequency hearing to exploit this. Dogs have smaller heads than us, so they need even higher frequency hearing for this direction finding to work.

IS THERE ANY TRUTH IN THE PHRASE 'FEED A COLD, STARVE A FEVER'?

This advice has been around since 1574, when dictionary writer John Withals wrote that 'fasting is a great remedie of feuer [fever]'. It was thought that fever was a symptom of an overactive metabolism and that eating would exacerbate this, while colds were caused by the body getting too cold. Both are false.

However, a study in 2002 at Amsterdam Academic Medical Centre found that fasting boosts the immune response that tackles bacterial infections (which commonly cause fever), whereas eating encourages killer T cells that attack cells infected with a virus, such as the cold virus.

ALAMY X3, THINKSTOCK X2

WHAT'S THE UPPER LIMIT ON HOW FAST SOMEONE CAN TALK?

The current record, in English at least, is 637 words per minute, a record held by English comedian and presenter Steve Woodmore. That's about four times faster than most people talk and twice as fast as we can read. The practical limit on speech is comprehension. Beyond 300 words per minute, you can't really make out the individual words clearly - record attempts are adjudicated by recording the speech and playing it back more slowly.

The theoretical upper limit on speed would be the rate at which the facial muscles can contract. Muscle fibres can't contract faster than about five times per second, so if you are repeating the mouth-stretching words "Wow oh wow oh", your lips couldn't manage to open and close more than 300 times per minute. Alternating between different muscles might let you interleave more words, but 637 definitely looks like it's quite close to the natural limit.

WHAT RESOLUTION DOES THE HUMAN EYE HAVE?

There are around six million cone cells on each retina and 90-126 million rods. Each receptor cell contributes a single point of information to the image; roughly like a pixel on a screen. So for a single snapshot, your eye's cone cells capture about six megapixels of colour information, while the rods manage 100 megapixels in black and white. Most of the cones are clustered around a central point called the fovea and the eye constantly roves to assemble a composite image. Dr Roger Clark of the US Geological Survey has calculated that the eye captures the equivalent of 576 megapixels.

WHAT PERCENTAGE OF MY BODY IS THE SAME AS FIVE YEARS AGO?

The idea that we replace every cell in our bodies every few years is a popular one - but incorrect nonetheless. Fat cells are replaced at about 10 per cent per year, but heart muscle cells turn over at just one per cent per year at age 25, declining to 0.5 percent by age 70. Even if you live to be 100, you'll still have more than half of the heart muscle cells you were born with. The neurones of the cerebral cortex and the cells in the lens of your eye are never normally replaced.

But even though the cells aren't completely replaced, they still change. Molecules are continually exchanged with the environment during ordinary metabolic processes. The water in your body turns over at about three litres per day. An adult has around 40 litres of body water, so that's 7.5 per cent per day. After two years, it's statistically unlikely that you have any of the same water molecules. But the calcium in your teeth is locked up forever.

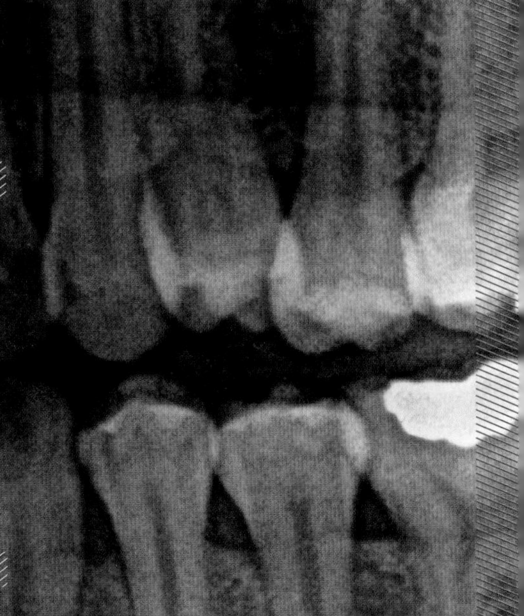

TOP TEN

TOP TEN DEADLIEST VIRUSES

(Source: World Health Organisation)

1. HIV
Deaths per year: 1.6 million
Spreads: via infected bodily fluids
Symptoms: weight loss, respiratory infections, rashes

2. Hepatitis B
Deaths per year: 600,000
Spreads: via infected blood
Symptoms: yellowing of eyes, vomiting, dark urine, abdominal pain

=3. Influenza
Deaths per year: 500,000
Spreads: via coughs and sneezes; also via bird droppings, blood and saliva
Symptoms: fever, aches, fatigue

=3. Hepatitis C
Deaths per year: 500,000
Spreads: through blood contact with an infected person
Symptoms: fever, stomach pain, depression, itchy skin, liver disease

5. Rotavirus
Deaths per year: 450,000
Spreads: through ingestion of contaminated stool
Symptoms: vomiting, diarrhoea, dehydration, fever

6. Measles
Deaths per year: 122,000
Spreads: through direct contact with an infected person
Symptoms: fever, white spots/red blotches, vomiting, diarrhoea

7. Hantavirus
Deaths per year: 70,000
Spreads: via rodent droppings
Symptoms: facial flushing, hypotension, respiratory and renal problems

8. Rabies
Deaths per year: 55,000
Spreads: via animal bites
Symptoms: acute pain, violent movements, depression, mania, inability to swallow water, coma

9. Yellow fever
Deaths per year: 30,000
Spreads: via mosquito bites
Symptoms: fever, bleeding into skin, slow heart, jaundice, coma

10. Dengue
Global deaths per year: 25,000
Spreads: via mosquito bites
Symptoms: fever, muscle pain, rash, circulatory failure, shock

WOULD A STARVING FAT PERSON LIVE LONGER THAN A STARVING THIN PERSON?

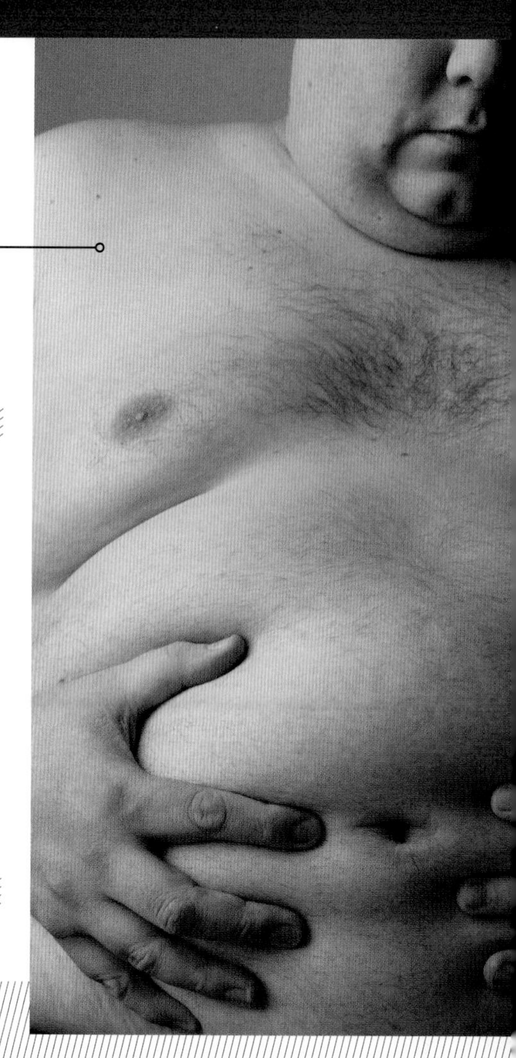

Possibly. When you stop eating, your body will exhaust the glycogen stored in the liver after about six hours and begin breaking down body fat into fatty acids for energy. But fatty acids can't cross the blood-brain barrier, so the brain needs another source of energy. Humans have a unique ability to convert fat into ketones to feed the brain. But a starving brain still needs about 10g of glucose per day and that has to come from muscle breakdown. A fat person will normally last longer, but 40 to 50 per cent weight loss is life threatening, regardless of your initial weight.

WHY DO WE MAKE THAT 'ATCHOO' SOUND WHEN WE SNEEZE?

A sneeze begins with a sudden inhalation. This is the 'Aaah' part of the sneeze. The 'Choo!' occurs on the exhale because most of the muscles in your body are reflexively contracting. This clamps your mouth shut until the pressure in your lungs rises too high and the air escapes in a burst. Since your tongue is pressing against the roof of your mouth, the air makes a 'ch' sound and, with your lips pursed, it emerges as an 'oo'.

WHY DO OUR FINGERS WRINKLE IN THE BATH?

It used to be thought that wrinkling was a purely passive process, caused by your fingers absorbing water so that the skin swelled up and became too big for the tissue it was anchored to. In fact, recent research has shown that it's the other way round: the tissues of the fingertips contract and pull the surrounding skin into wrinkles. This is an active mechanism controlled by the nervous system. Since your body is deliberately wrinkling your fingers, that suggests there must be a reason for it and a study at Newcastle University showed that wrinkled fingers are better at gripping wet objects. As well as allowing our ancestors to grapple with wriggling fish, this would have helped them to keep their balance on wet rocks because our toes get wrinkly too.

WHY DO WE STRETCH WHEN WE WAKE UP?

When you sleep, your muscles lose tone and fluid tends to pool along your back. Stretching helps to massage fluid gently back into the normal position. Also, your muscles protect themselves from over-extension by inhibiting the nerve impulses as they approach their limit. Over time, the safety mechanism becomes increasingly restrictive. Stretching briefly takes your muscles outside their normal range. This recalibrates the feedback mechanisms that determine their normal amount of motion.

WHY DOES ARTHRITIS TEND TO HURT MORE WHEN IT'S COLD AND WET?

No-one knows why, yet this connection has enough evidence to set clinicians wondering. The weather cannot affect the arthritis itself but might possibly make the symptoms worse. One theory blames the drop in barometric pressure associated with bad weather. The idea is that as pressure falls, tissues around the joints swell, rather like a balloon expanding when the air pressure drops. However, any such effect would be extremely small and has never been directly detected.

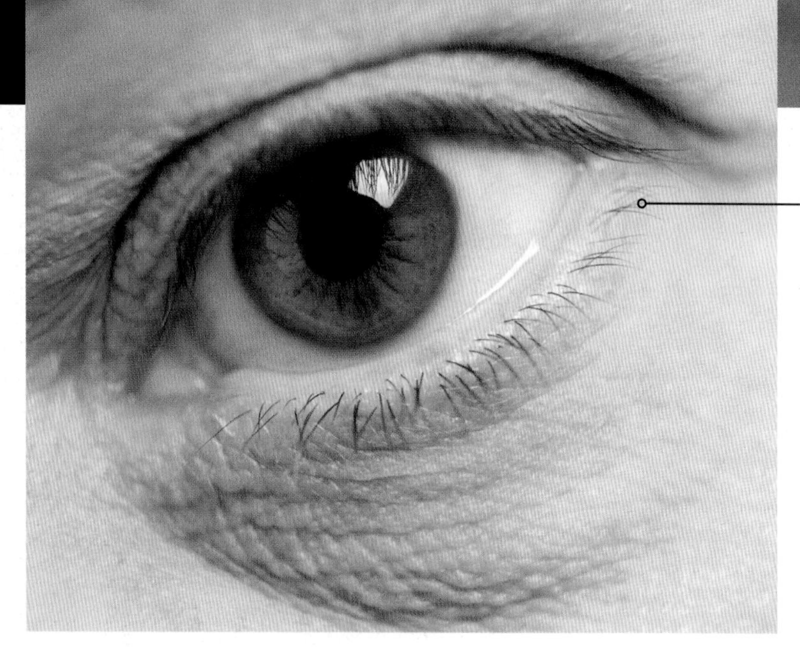

HOW DO BAGS FORM UNDER OUR EYES?

There hasn't been much research to establish whether this is caused by a lack of sleep or by something else. The skin under our eyes is very thin, meaning fluid retention there can cause it to sag. It's possible that, when we sleep, this fluid has a chance to drain away, but diet may also play a part. Staying up late is often associated with drinking alcohol or coffee or eating salty junk food. Any of these could be the real cause of eye bags; we don't really know for sure.

IS TOMATO KETCHUP GOOD FOR YOUR HEART?

Tomatoes and tomato juice are known to reduce blood levels of low-density lipoprotein – or 'bad cholesterol' – and so reduce the risk of heart disease. But can a thick dollop of ketchup have any such positive effect? Apparently it can. The pigment that provides the red colouring in tomatoes is lycopene, an anti-oxidant that helps prevent cell damage and inhibits heart disease. Ketchup contains lycopene, with organic and dark red varieties containing the most. In some experiments, people's levels of LDL fell in just a few weeks of eating extra ketchup. Whether it's as good as the real thing is another matter, since fresh tomatoes also contain other healthy ingredients.

THINKSTOCK X3, ALAMY

WHAT IS THE FUNCTION OF THE HUMAN APPENDIX?

The appendix was classically regarded as unnecessary - even its name implies that it is a leftover bit. It's a thin tube, about the size of half a pencil, that sticks out of the cecum, which is a pouch at the start of the large intestine. Charles Darwin thought that our ancestors ate a lot more plant roughage than us and needed a larger cecum to digest it, so the appendix was originally a useful compartment of the intestine that had dwindled through millions of years of disuse. Koalas, which eat very indigestible leaves, have a two-metre-long cecum that is essentially a giant appendix.

Certainly it's true that you can amputate the appendix without any obvious long-term consequences for the patient. But that same argument applies to a toe. Being able to get along without something doesn't mean it's entirely useless. Recent research that compared the intestines of 361 mammals found that 50 different, quite unrelated, species have an appendix. This means that the appendix must have evolved independently at least 32 times, which suggests it must be doing something useful.

It's now thought that the appendix acts as an emergency bunker for your gut bacteria to shelter in. Its narrow opening and out-of-the-way position mean that bacterial infections don't normally get inside it. So after diarrhoea has flushed the last of any bad bacteria out of your intestines, the good guys can emerge from the appendix and re-colonise your colon.

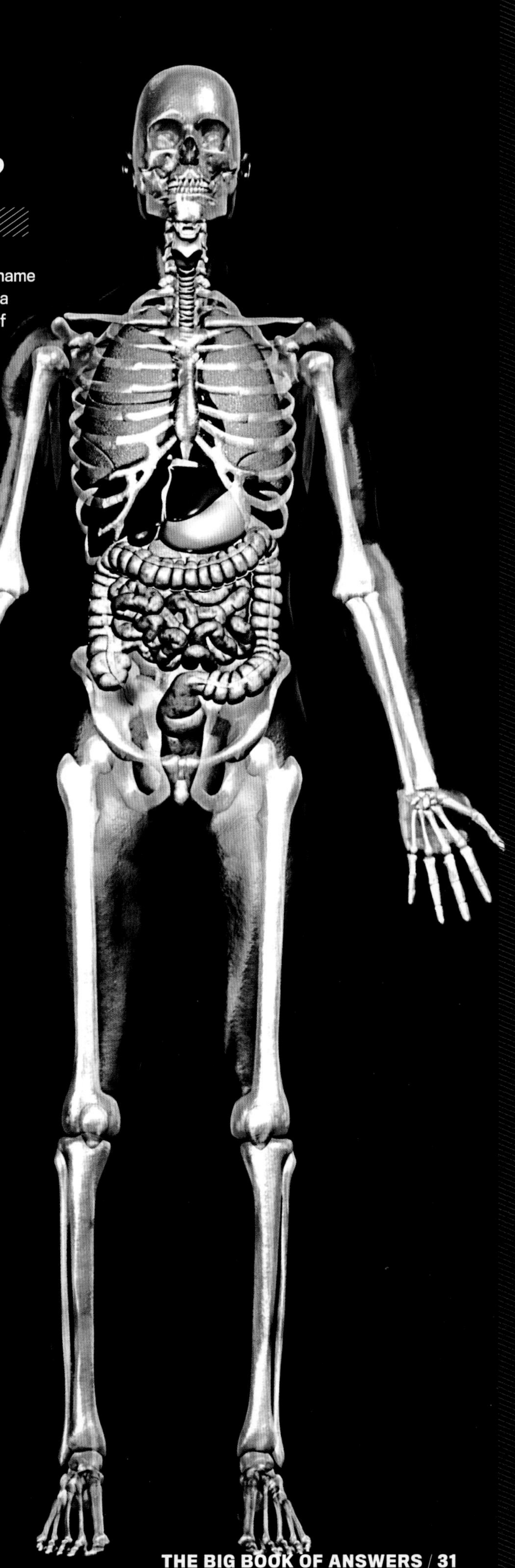

100,000

kilometres (62,000 miles) is the total length of blood vessels in the human body. That's nearly two and a half times around the Earth!

DOES A BALD MAN LOSE MORE HEAT FROM HIS HEAD THAN A MAN WITH HAIR?

Yes. Hair insulates your head by trapping a layer of air close to your skin, which prevents heat loss through convection. This is important when it is windy. A 2008 study in Switzerland measured how much heat motorcycle riders lose from their heads, using special thermal manikins. They found that the rate of heat loss was proportional to the wind speed, but the manikins that wore a wig under a helmet lost half as much heat as the bald ones.

HOW MUCH CAN A HUMAN SWEAT?

During exercise, most of us will sweat no more than 1.4 litres per hour. The highest sweat rate recorded by an athlete was 3.7 litres per hour by the Cuban-born marathon runner Alberto Salazar in 1984. But unless you drink to replenish lost fluid and electrolytes, you will suffer seizure and heart failure once you have lost around 25 percent of your bodyweight in sweat. That's about 17.5 litres for a 70kg adult – but you'd be in no shape to run quite a while before that.

SCIENCE PHOTO LIBRARY, ALAMY X2, THINKSTOCK X2

IS IT GOOD TO LIE IN AT THE WEEKEND?

Some studies suggest that people who sleep more than nine hours have an increased chance of suffering illness or accident. But it isn't clear whether this is caused by too much sleep, or if it's simply that people predisposed to become ill are also more likely to spend longer in bed – for example, because they are depressed.

In any case, this is for people that routinely oversleep. Catching up on lost sleep at the weekend doesn't do you any harm by itself, but it may not be enough to repair damage caused by inadequate sleep during the week. A 2013 study at Pennsylvania State University College of Medicine found that catching up on lost sleep reduced the levels of stress hormones in their blood. But it didn't improve their performance in tests that measured concentration.

WHY DO WE HAVE LINES ON THE PALMS OF OUR HANDS?

So that we can scrunch our hands into a fist, or other complex shapes, without excessive stretching or leaving bags of loose skin – think about how much movement occurs when you're typing, holding a cup or doing chores. The lines are called 'palmar flexion creases' and develop before birth. Most people have two main lines across the palm but some have a single 'Simian crease'. This can be inherited normally on either one or both hands, but is also associated with Down's syndrome and other conditions. Palmistry claims the lines reveal your personality traits, but there is no evidence for this.

WHY DO WE HAVE EYEBROWS?

Originally to keep rain and sweat out of our eyes. As a species we humans rely on our sight more than any other sense, and water can seriously blur vision. Eyebrows may also deflect debris and shield our eyes from the Sun. So while we slowly evolved to lose most of our body hair, our eyelashes and eyebrows remained.

But eyebrows then took on another function: communication. Facial expressions convey meaning and emotions in ways that are hard to fake, and the eyebrows exaggerate expressions. Even in cartoons, a simple line above the eyes is enough to denote anger, fear or surprise in a face, and experiments have shown that we can recognise a familiar face more easily when the eyes are blanked out than when the eyebrows are. So if you're tempted to redesign your eyebrows by shaving or plucking them, do remember their many uses.

Who lives here?

Sadly, no-one these days. This is what remains of what was once a lively town. Tourists visiting Villa Epecuén in Argentina would head for Lake Epecuén to bathe in the salty waters, hoping it would cure their ills.

But the lake that enabled this resort to grow engulfed it in 1985 when it flooded. "The period since the 1970s was exceptionally wet, and so the resort, established in the 1920s, became flooded in spite of a dam being built to try and protect it," says Professor Andrew Goudie, Emeritus Professor of Geography at the University of Oxford. "Now the climate has reverted to what it was like in the earlier 20th century and so the lake has started to dry out, exposing the formerly flooded resort."

For more great pictures, follow us on http://pinterest.com/sciencefocus

SPACE

During the past century, advances in technology have enabled astronomers to make great leaps into understanding not only our Solar System, but the Milky Way and other galaxies beyond...

HOW FAST IS THE UNIVERSE EXPANDING?

The expansion of the Universe is unusual in that the further we look, the faster galaxies appear to be racing away from us. This is captured in Hubble's Constant, the standard way of measuring the cosmic expansion.

Analysis of the light from distant stars and galaxies reveals both their speed and distance, and these imply that the cosmic expansion rate is surprisingly sluggish: the speed of recession increases by just 1km/h for every 13 light-years of distance. As such, we can all but forget about the cosmic expansion on the scale of our Galaxy, where it's overwhelmed by gravity in any case.

Only on the largest scales does the expansion of the Universe start to really get up steam, with the most distant visible galaxies, which lie many billions of light-years away, receding from us at sizeable fractions of the speed of light.

DO ALL PLANETS SPIN THE SAME WAY?

Most planets (including Earth) rotate anti-clockwise when viewed from above their north poles. This reflects the original rotation of the proto-stellar disc that formed the Sun and planets. However, Venus rotates clockwise when viewed above its north pole while Uranus's rotation axis is tilted almost perpendicular to its orbital plane. The most common theory as to why the rotations of Venus and Uranus are different from those of the other planets is that they were involved in violent collisions soon after their formation.

WHAT IS THE CHANCE OF AN ASTEROID HITTING EARTH?

There are probably several million asteroids with the potential for smashing into planet Earth. But very large asteroids, which would have catastrophic consequences if they hit us, are thankfully very rare. Astronomers estimate that one of these monster asteroids (like the one that wiped out the dinosaurs) should fall to Earth once every 100 million years or so.

An object about 100m across should arrive every 1,000 years, although thousands of kilograms of tiny meteoroids land on Earth each day. However, most go unnoticed because they fall in unpopulated areas or into the sea. The chances of you being killed by an asteroid are very small indeed – much smaller than the risks you take driving a car or crossing the road.

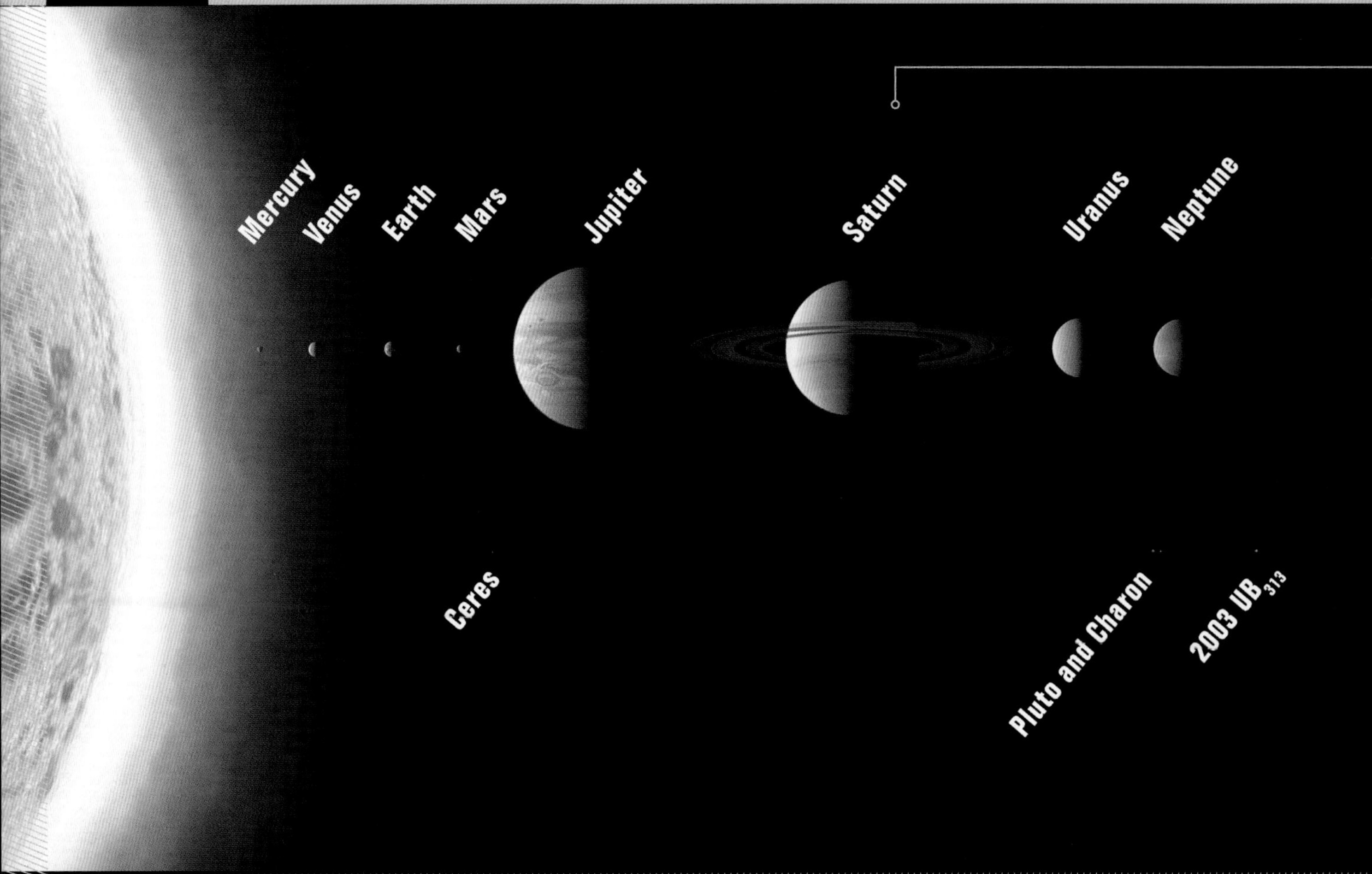

HOW ARE LIGHT-YEARS MEASURED?

A light-year is the distance travelled by light in one year. It is commonly used as a unit of distance in astronomy. Astronomers use various methods to determine distances. Within the Solar System, distances can be found using radar, using simple trigonometry or by tracking orbital motions around the Sun. For relatively nearby stars, distances can be found by watching their tiny wobbling in the sky caused by the Earth's yearly journey around the Sun, or by analysing the orbits of binary stars. Further afield, direct distance measurements are not possible and astronomers resort to indirect methods.

There methods mostly involve objects called 'standard candles'. These are objects (stars, novae or supernovae, for example) for which the astronomer already knows the actual brightness. Comparing this with the brightness seen here on Earth reveals the object's distance. Since the Universe is expanding, the more distant an object, the faster it is moving away from us. So for really remote galaxies, astronomers estimate distance using a measure of their object's motion called its 'redshift'.

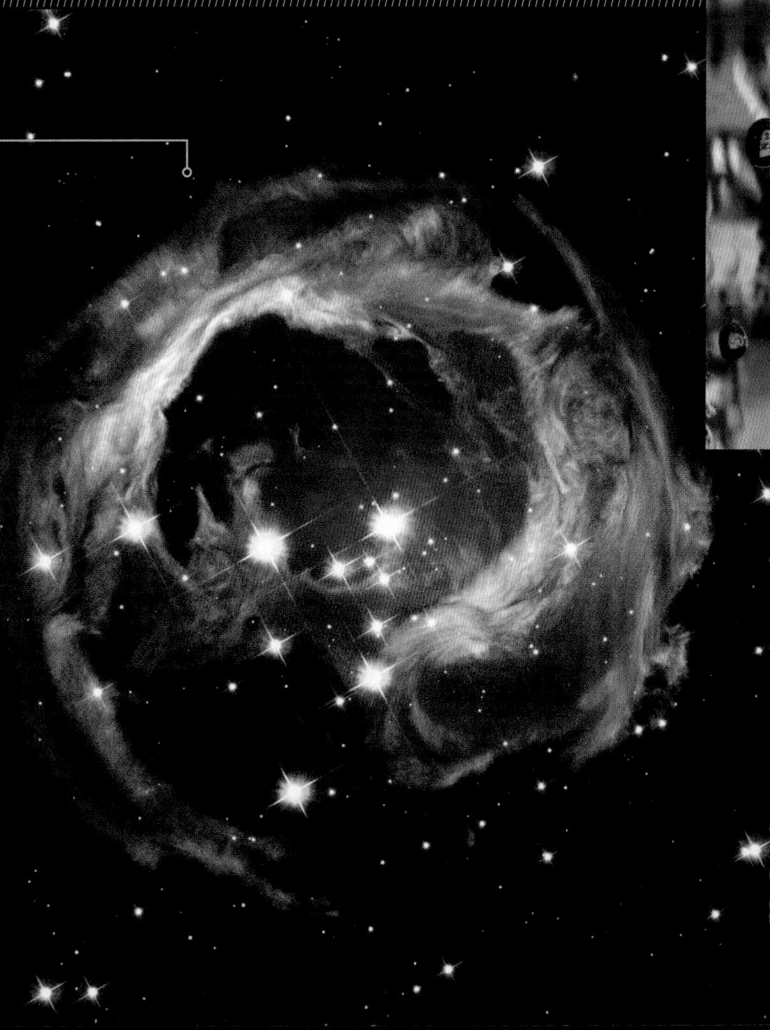

COURTESY OF IAU, NASA/HUBBLE, THINKSTOCK, ALAMY

WHO NAMES THE STARS AND THE PLANETS?

The International Astronomical Union (IAU) oversees the names of celestial objects. Star-naming usually follows catalogues with names like General Catalogue or the Henry Draper Catalogue. The star's name is made up of letters representing the specific catalogue and numbers denoting its position. You end up with names like HD 41004 and GC 28804. Amateur astronomers still know bright stars by their traditional names, such as Vega or Betelguese.

Extrasolar planets began to be discovered in the mid-1990s, requiring a whole load of new names. Each new planet is named by its discoverer, subject to approval by an IAU working group. For example, the extrasolar planet Kaohsiung was named by amateur astronomer Tsai Yuan-sheng after his home city. Names can be anything within reason. IAU guidelines prefer nomenclature of a single word. The name should also be decent, non-commercial and sufficiently unlike existing ones. And for all you vain people out there, no, the IAU doesn't sell personalised star or planet names.

HOW WOULD FIZZY DRINKS BEHAVE IN SPACE?

Without gravity, there is no density gradient within the drink, so its bubbles float around randomly inside the liquid. Occasionally a bubble strikes another with enough force to overcome the surface tension and they merge, so over time the bubbles coalesce into a few large bubbles that squash the others into a sort of static foam.

HOW FREQUENTLY DO THE PLANETS IN OUR SOLAR SYSTEM LINE UP?

The answer to this question depends on how we define 'line up'. Because the planets orbit the Sun with slightly different orbital inclinations, it is extremely unlikely they will ever align perfectly – the odds of this happening are something like one in 86 billion trillion trillion trillion years! However, if by 'line up' we just mean that some of the planets appear close together in the sky, then this occurs fairly regularly. For example, the five naked-eye planets cluster within 25 degrees or less of each other once every 57 years, on average. The last time this happened was on 5 May 2000; before that it was 4 February 1962, and it will happen next on 8 September 2040. But these are not true planetary 'alignments', they are simply interesting and beautiful groupings of the planets in the sky.

WHY ARE SOLAR ECLIPSES RARER THAN LUNAR ECLIPSES?

Solar eclipses are not actually rarer than lunar eclipses - in fact, they occur in about equal numbers, usually about two of each per year. For example, between 2000BC to 3000AD there will be 11,898 solar eclipses and 12,064 lunar eclipses. However, at any one location on Earth, it is much less common to see a solar eclipse than a lunar one. And the reason for this is entirely due to geometry. A lunar eclipse, when the Moon moves through the shadow of the Earth, is visible from wherever the Moon is above the horizon, which is over half of the Earth. However, when the Moon appears to move in front of the Sun during a solar eclipse, the shadow cast by the Moon is much smaller than Earth. It's only about 480km (300 miles) wide when cast onto the Earth's surface. Solar eclipses are therefore only visible from within a narrow path across the Earth, making it difficult to get to a location to see one. This is why they are visible less often from any given location.

DID YOU KNOW?
The Salyut Space Station, launched in 1974, was armed with a 23mm cannon for defence.

WHEN WILL THE MILKY WAY AND ANDROMEDA COLLIDE?

It has been known for decades that our closest large galactic neighbour, the Andromeda Galaxy, is heading toward our own Milky Way at around 120km/s. But until recently, astronomers were unsure whether Andromeda would score a direct hit, a near miss or a glancing blow. While it's quite easy to measure the relative approach speed of Andromeda, it's very difficult to measure its exact direction of motion. But, using the Hubble Space Telescope, astronomers have finally pinned down its trajectory. It will collide head-on with the Milky Way, in about four billion years' time.

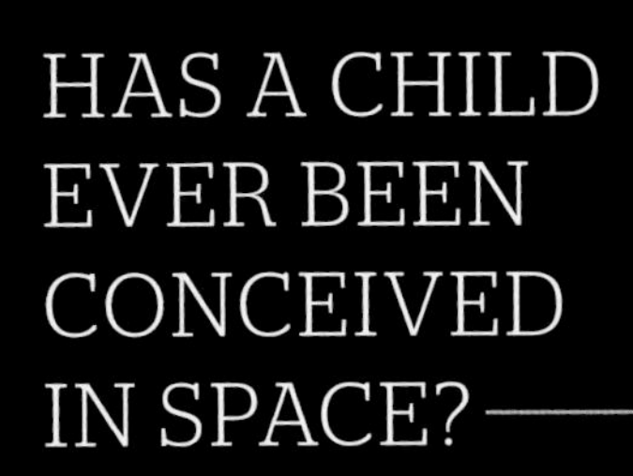

HAS A CHILD EVER BEEN CONCEIVED IN SPACE?

No-one has ever had sex in space, much less got themselves pregnant, according to both NASA and the Russian Space Agency. Spacecraft are crowded and cramped, with virtually no privacy. Astronauts are regarded as on duty 24-hours a day and would be unlikely to risk their privileged flight status with this sort of unsanctioned behaviour.

DO COMETS MAKE A SOUND?

A famous movie tagline chillingly reminds us that "in space, no-one can hear you scream". This is true since for sound waves to be transmitted and eventually register as 'sound' in our ears, they need a medium through which to travel. That medium can be any material (solid, liquid or gas). Space is almost, but not quite, a perfect vacuum, so comets are silent, just like everything else in space.

COULD A BLACK HOLE SWALLOW AN ENTIRE GALAXY?

This is extremely unlikely. Although astronomers think that supermassive black holes exist at the cores of perhaps all galaxies, they are actually very small in comparison to the size of their hosts. This means that, while gravity is very strong near a black hole, their gravitational pull is comparatively weak far from the galactic core.

So although such black holes dominate the inner regions of galaxies, and often power extreme energy production, they don't have the strength to suck in entire galaxies.

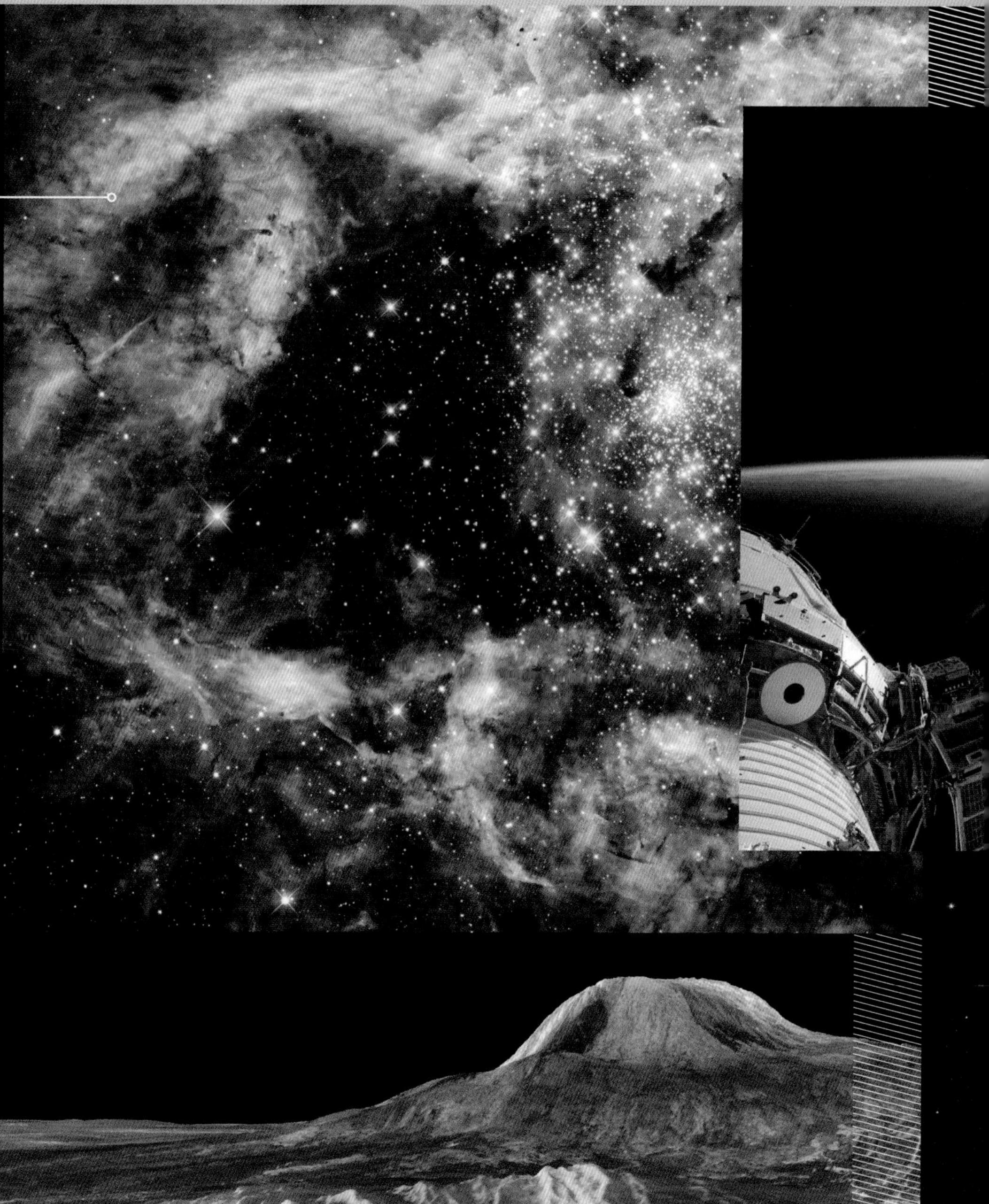

WHY AREN'T THERE MORE STARS?

Astronomers estimate there may be 1 septillion (10^{24}) stars in the observable Universe. As huge as that number is, our understanding of how clouds of gas and dust collapse to form stars says there should be 10 times as many. However, researchers in the US have found a weak magnetic field in a distant cloud disrupting star formation, which could explain the discrepancy.

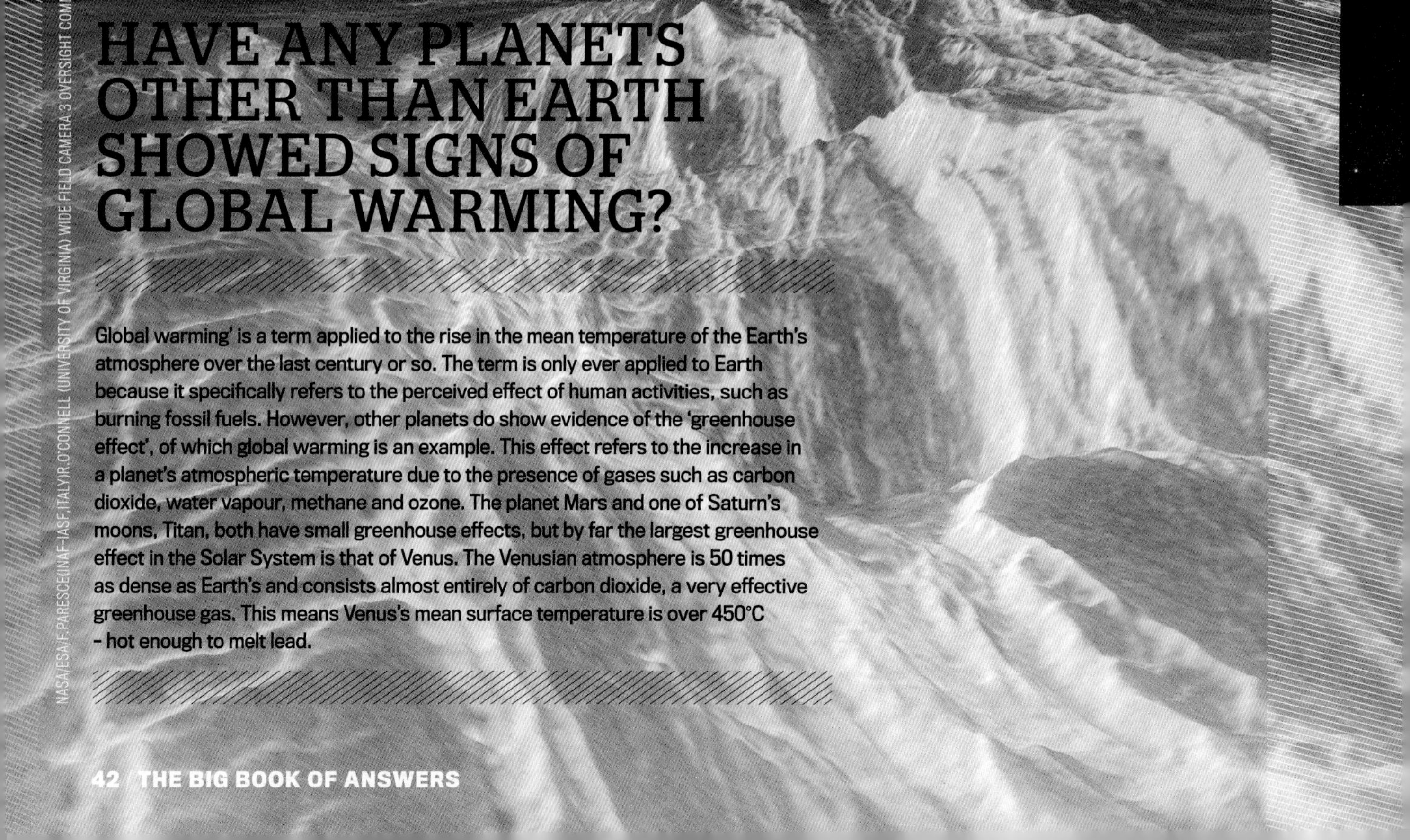

HAVE ANY PLANETS OTHER THAN EARTH SHOWED SIGNS OF GLOBAL WARMING?

Global warming' is a term applied to the rise in the mean temperature of the Earth's atmosphere over the last century or so. The term is only ever applied to Earth because it specifically refers to the perceived effect of human activities, such as burning fossil fuels. However, other planets do show evidence of the 'greenhouse effect', of which global warming is an example. This effect refers to the increase in a planet's atmospheric temperature due to the presence of gases such as carbon dioxide, water vapour, methane and ozone. The planet Mars and one of Saturn's moons, Titan, both have small greenhouse effects, but by far the largest greenhouse effect in the Solar System is that of Venus. The Venusian atmosphere is 50 times as dense as Earth's and consists almost entirely of carbon dioxide, a very effective greenhouse gas. This means Venus's mean surface temperature is over 450°C – hot enough to melt lead.

NASA/ESA/F. PARESCE(INAF-IASF, ITALY)/R. O'CONNELL (UNIVERSITY OF VIRGINIA) WIDE FIELD CAMERA 3 OVERSIGHT COMMITTEE, NASA/JPL, NASA/STS-129, ESO

WHAT TIME ZONE DO THEY USE ON THE INTERNATIONAL SPACE STATION?

International Space Station crews experience a sunset or a sunrise every 45 minutes. New members arrive acclimatised to Kazakhstan time, having departed from the Baikonur Cosmodrome. With so much scope for chronological confusion, it's no wonder that the ISS needs to be locked to a consistent time. The zone of choice is Coordinated Universal Time (UTC), which is equivalent to GMT.

ARE NEW GALAXIES STILL FORMING?

It appears that new-born galaxies are alive and well in the Universe. Most galaxies formed very soon after the Big Bang and astronomers have known for some time that the rate of galaxy formation has steadily declined through time. When the Universe was young, galaxies were forming regularly, but over time fewer and fewer were born as these babies grew up into adult galaxies much like our own Milky Way.

Recently, however, astronomers have found evidence that both dwarf galaxies and their more massive cousins are still forming in the Universe. Some may be younger than one billion years. These galaxies seem to have remained in an embryonic state as cold clouds of hydrogen and helium gas for most of the Universe's history. Why they took so long to form into galaxies, and what it was that made them do is, is currently unknown.

TOP TEN

LONGEST HUMAN SPACE FLIGHTS

1. Valeri Polyakov
Duration: 437.7 days
Country: Russia
Mission: Mir
Year: 1994-95

2. Sergei Avdeyev
Duration: 379.6 days
Country: Russia
Mission: Mir
Year: 1998-99

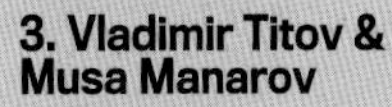

3. Vladimir Titov & Musa Manarov
Duration: 364.9 days
Country: Soviet Union
Mission: Mir
Year: 1987-88

4. Yuri Romanenko
Duration: 326 days
Country: Soviet Union/Russia
Mission: Mir
Year: 1988-89

5. Sergei Krikalev
Duration: 312 days
Country: Soviet Union/Russia
Mission: Mir
Year: 1991-92

6. Valeri Polyakov
Duration: 240 days
Country: Soviet Union
Mission: Mir
Year: 1988-89

7. Leonid Kizim, Vladimir Solovyov & Oleg Atkov
Duration: 237 days
Country: Soviet Union
Mission: Salyut 7 Space Station
Year: 1984

8. Mikhail Tyurin & Michael Lopez-Allegria
Duration: 215 days
Country: Russia & USA
Mission: International Space Station
Year: 2006-07

9. Anatoli Berezovoy & Valentin Lebedev
Duration: 211 days
Country: Soviet Union
Mission: Salyut 7 Space Station
Year: 1994-95

10. Nikolai Budarin & Talgat Musabayev
Duration: 207 days
Country: Russia
Mission: Mir
Year: 1998

HOW RAPIDLY IS THE UNIVERSE EXPANDING?

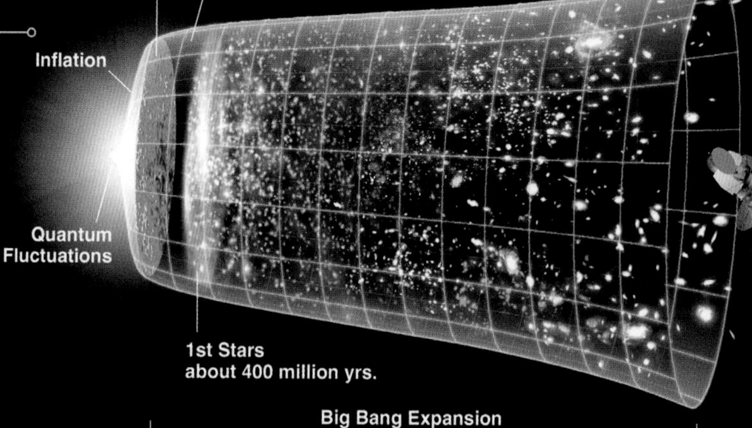

Explanations of how the Universe expands often draw analogies with a balloon being inflated, with coins stuck on to represent clusters of galaxies bound together by gravity. While this gets across the idea that it's the space between clumps of matter that's expanding, it doesn't capture the special way in which the expansion takes place. The cosmos expands 'isotropically', keeping the same appearance in all directions.

This means that on the largest scales, every point moves away from every other according to a simple law which states that their relative speed is proportional to the distance between them. This is measured by the so-called Hubble constant, which is worked out by observing the speed of galaxies moving away from us by their distance. The results show that on the biggest scales, every point in the Universe moves away from every other at a speed of 1km/h for every 13 light-years of distance.

HOW DO WE KNOW HOW HOT THE SUN IS?

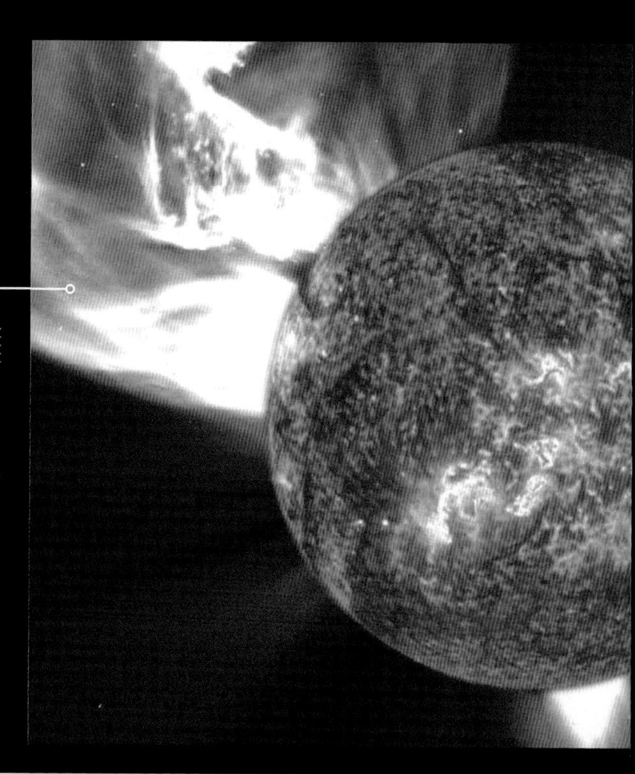

The Sun is a scorching 5,500°C. There are several ways that we can measure its temperature. First, we can measure the amount of radiation hitting Earth and use the Sun's distance and size to calculate how hot it must be. The Sun's light also has a particular spectrum and its shape, as well as the wavelength of light where most energy is emitted, reveals the Sun's temperature.

But the most accurate method relies on the fact that elements in the solar atmosphere absorb radiation. Which wavelengths are absorbed, and by how much, also depends on the temperature. The temperature at the centre of the Sun can be calculated using our knowledge of nuclear physics. It's a sweltering 15,700,000°C.

HOW MANY PLANETS WILL BE ENGULFED WHEN THE SUN DIES?

In five billion years, the Sun will expand to become a 'red giant'. It will engulf the planets Mercury and Venus, but the Earth's fate is less clear. As the Sun swells up to 250 times its present size, it will lose more than a third of its mass in a strong 'stellar wind'. This will cause the planets' orbits to widen significantly so that the Earth may just escape the out-rushing Sun. However, the Earth's gravity could tug the Sun's surface just enough to create a tidal effect and pull the Earth back in to a closer orbit. Even so, our planet will have been long dead; three billion years from now, the Sun's energy output will have evaporated the oceans.

WHAT DOES DARK ENERGY DO?

Dark energy, identified by astronomers in the 1990s, acts like a form of anti-gravity. While its origins are unknown, observations reveal that it has a repulsive effect that is negligible at human scales but which gets stronger with distance, propelling the expansion of the Universe over the largest distances.

13.1 billion years is the time it took for light to reach us from the most distant galaxy known. The light was emitted only 700 million years after the Big Bang.

WOULD IT BE POSSIBLE TO SEND A PROBE INTO A BLACK HOLE?

It would be possible but a bit fruitless. As your probe approaches the black hole's event horizon, beyond which it is lost forever, the difference in gravitational attraction between its top and bottom will be enough to tear it apart. Oddly, though, the more massive the black hole the less this tidal force, so your probe might just survive beyond the event horizon of a really big black hole.

Even so, due to the warping of space-time around the black hole, your probe will experience time slowing down relative to the 'outside world'. For you, watching your probe descend, you would see it slowing down until it becomes frozen in time at the event horizon. As a result, any radio transmissions it makes will be impossible to detect.

ORVAR ATLI THORGEIRSSON

How is an ice cave formed?

Found in the Skaftafell region of south-east Iceland, this cave has been formed underneath the Svínafellsjökull glacier, which slowly moves down the slopes of Öræfajökull, Iceland's tallest active volcano. As it moves, some of the ice encounters rock, and the resulting friction and the relative warmth of the rock cause melting. Added to this, meltwater from the glacier's surface works its way through ice cracks to the cave beneath. In the warmer summer months, there's enough meltwater to flow through the cave.

"The ripples on the ceiling and walls are called 'scallops' and are sculpted by the flow of water," says Dr George Veni, Executive Director of the National Cave and Karst Research Institute in the US. "Glacier caves are geologically young features - some do not exist for more than a year or two before collapsing."

Air bubbles are squeezed out of the ice as it moves. This allows light to penetrate, causing the ice to appear blue because it absorbs more light at the red end of the spectrum.

For more great pictures, follow us on http://pinterest.com/sciencefocus

GENETICS & EVOLUTION

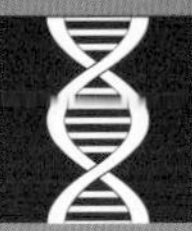

When did life first evolve? How many people have ever lived? Could a Neanderthal be cloned? Discover fascinating facts about genetics and delve deeper into evolution

WHAT CAUSES LEFT-HANDEDNESS?

Being left-handed is the result of genes and environment. About 50 per cent more males than females are left-handed. Also 17 per cent of twins are, compared with about 10 per cent in general. The 'vanishing twin' hypothesis suggests that left-handers were originally a twin, but the right-handed foetus failed to develop.

Brain dominance also appears to play a part. Most people are right-handed and have language controlled by the left hemisphere, and most left-handers are the opposite. However, some left-handers have language processing in the left hemisphere, or in both.

The genetic basis for left-handedness is complicated. Even if both parents are left-handed, there is only a 26 per cent chance of their child being left-handed. Possessing the 'LRRTM1' gene increases the chances, but only if it is inherited from the father.

But whether you become left-handed or not is also dependent on development. It may be influenced by levels of testosterone or oestrogen during pregnancy; early experience with holding and throwing things can affect later hand use. And, finally, damage to the right hand can make people left-handed.

WHY DO WE HAVE SO MANY TEETH?

Adult humans have 32 teeth, which isn't all that many – the Virginia opossum has 50 teeth and some dolphins have more than 250. The problem is that our jaws are too small for the teeth we have. A 2011 study at the University of Kent has suggested that this may be because we aren't hunter-gatherers any more. Agriculture and cooking have given us much softer food to eat and our jawbone has evolved to a shorter, wider shape more suited to that diet. Until we also evolve smaller teeth or fewer of them, we'll have to rely on the orthodontist to sort out the overcrowding.

THINKSTOCK X3

DID YOU KNOW?

Between 2000 and 2050, the proportion of the world's population over the age of 60 is estimated to double to 22%.

WHY DO HUMANS WALK UPRIGHT?

Probably because it saves energy. The once popular idea that walking upright evolved to regulate body heat in hot weather has recently been knocked on the head by mathematical simulations that suggest there was insufficient evolutionary pressure for heat control to be the answer. Other popular theories include freeing our ancestors' hands for using tools or carrying food, and that walking upright makes it possible to wade through deeper water.

Most compelling, though, are experiments in which both humans and chimpanzees walked on treadmills while their oxygen consumption and walking were measured. The chimps varied a lot, but on average used the same amount of energy when walking on all fours as on two legs. The humans used 75 per cent less energy when walking upright than the chimps used on all fours. So walking upright can save precious energy.

WHAT'S THE SOONEST LIFE COULD HAVE EVOLVED AFTER THE BIG BANG?

That depends on what you mean by 'life', but it's reasonable to say that the absolute minimum requirement is the existence of molecules made from relatively heavy elements like carbon, oxygen and nitrogen. In that case, we can certainly exclude the existence of life for several hundred million years after the Big Bang. That's how long it took for the appearance of the first stars, the thermonuclear reactions of which are needed to 'cook' the hydrogen and helium formed in the Big Bang into heavier elements. These first-generation stars are believed to have been far more massive than our Sun and to have burned brighter but for much less long - perhaps just a few million years before exploding. So that puts the earliest possible date for the emergence of life at around several hundred million years after the Big Bang.

WHY AREN'T WE GENETICALLY IDENTICAL TO OUR SIBLINGS?

In sexually reproducing species, eggs and sperm are created in a process called meiosis. Most human cells contain 23 pairs of chromosomes. In meiosis, the two chromosomes in a pair are split apart, making an egg or sperm which has just single chromosomes. When an egg and sperm fuse, the chromosomes from each come together to make new pairs. In a process called 'crossing over', their genes are shuffled so that the resulting new cell is a unique mixture of the genes inherited from each parent.

That's the mechanism, but the deeper question here is why, in evolutionary terms, it is worth so many plants and animals going through this extraordinarily complex process at all? There are two main theories. Firstly, that it helps with DNA repair and avoids errors; secondly, that it increases genetic diversity, which is essential if creatures are to be able to adapt in changing environments.

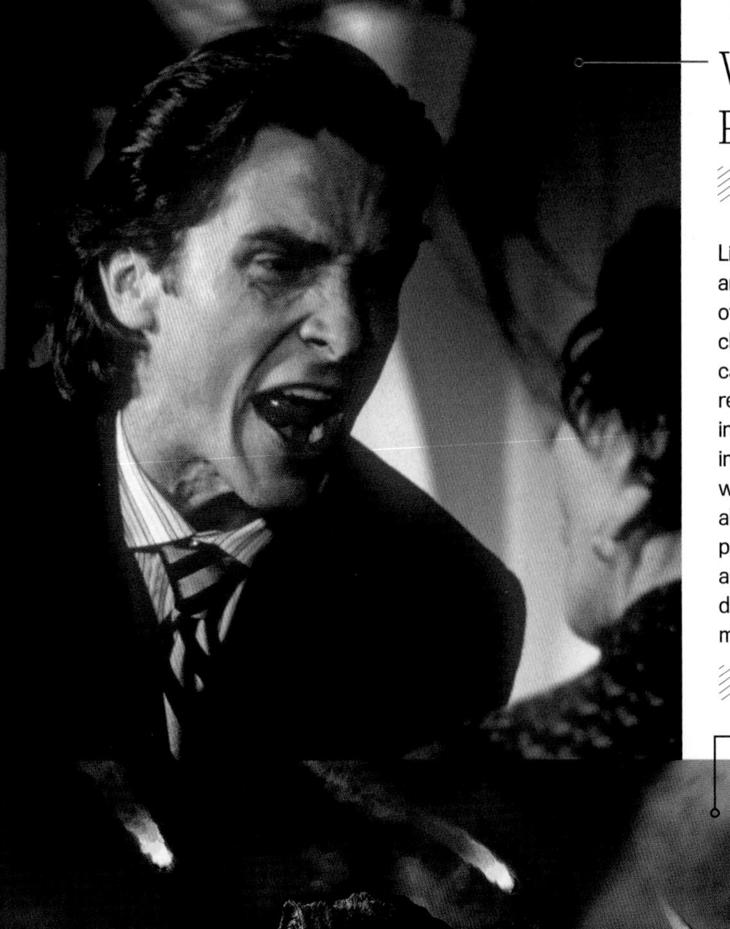

WHAT CAUSES PSYCHOPATHY?

Like many other conditions, psychopathy is a mixture of genetics and environment. From twin studies, we know that the heritability of psychopathic traits may be as much as 50 per cent and that the characteristic callousness, antisocial behaviour and lack of empathy can be detected as early as 9 or 10 years of age. One of the genes responsible has even been identified. It is a variant of a gene involved in transporting one of the brain's neurotransmitters, called serotonin, in and out of the synapses (the tiny gaps between nerve cells). Children with this variant are more likely to show psychopathic behaviours if they also have a deprived childhood. It is certainly possible to have a genetic predisposition to psychopathy and grow up without becoming uncaring and dangerous to others. It is the devastating effects of cruelty and abuse during childhood that is likely to bring out the worst traits and produce the murderous monsters that we associate with the term 'psychopath'.

IS IT ONLY HUMANS THAT HAVE MADE ANIMALS EXTINCT?

Not at all. Until two million years ago, there were no humans, so all extinctions before that were caused by something else. For mass extinction events, such as those at the end of the Permian and Cretaceous eras, this may have been a catastrophe such as an asteroid impact. But the bulk of evolutionary progress is driven by one animal out-competing its close relative and driving it to extinction. We evolved from primates, which evolved from four-legged mammals, which evolved from fish, which evolved from invertebrates. Modern examples of all of these animals still exist, but the specific species that were our direct ancestors do not, because they were driven to extinction. That process continues: for example, the red squirrel is being driven extinct by the grey squirrel.

WHAT DETERMINES LIFE SPAN?

Humans live for about 80 years, mice only a few years, some insects only a day – what determines these life spans has long been debated. The 19th-century theory of 'programmed death' suggested there were evolutionary advantages to older individuals dying because they leave more space and food for youngsters.

This theory is now generally rejected in favour of two other theories. 'Mutation accumulation theory' builds on the idea that mutations that cause an animal to die when very young are weeded out by natural selection, while those which cause older animals to die accumulate, leaving older animals more susceptible to dying.

Finally, according to antagonistic pleiotropy theory, mutations that are beneficial when you're young could also be harmful if they act later in life, which ultimately influences life span. For instance, a mutation that results in rapid cell growth might help you heal faster, but could increase the risk of cancer later on.

DOES YOUR BLOOD GROUP AFFECT YOUR PERSONALITY?

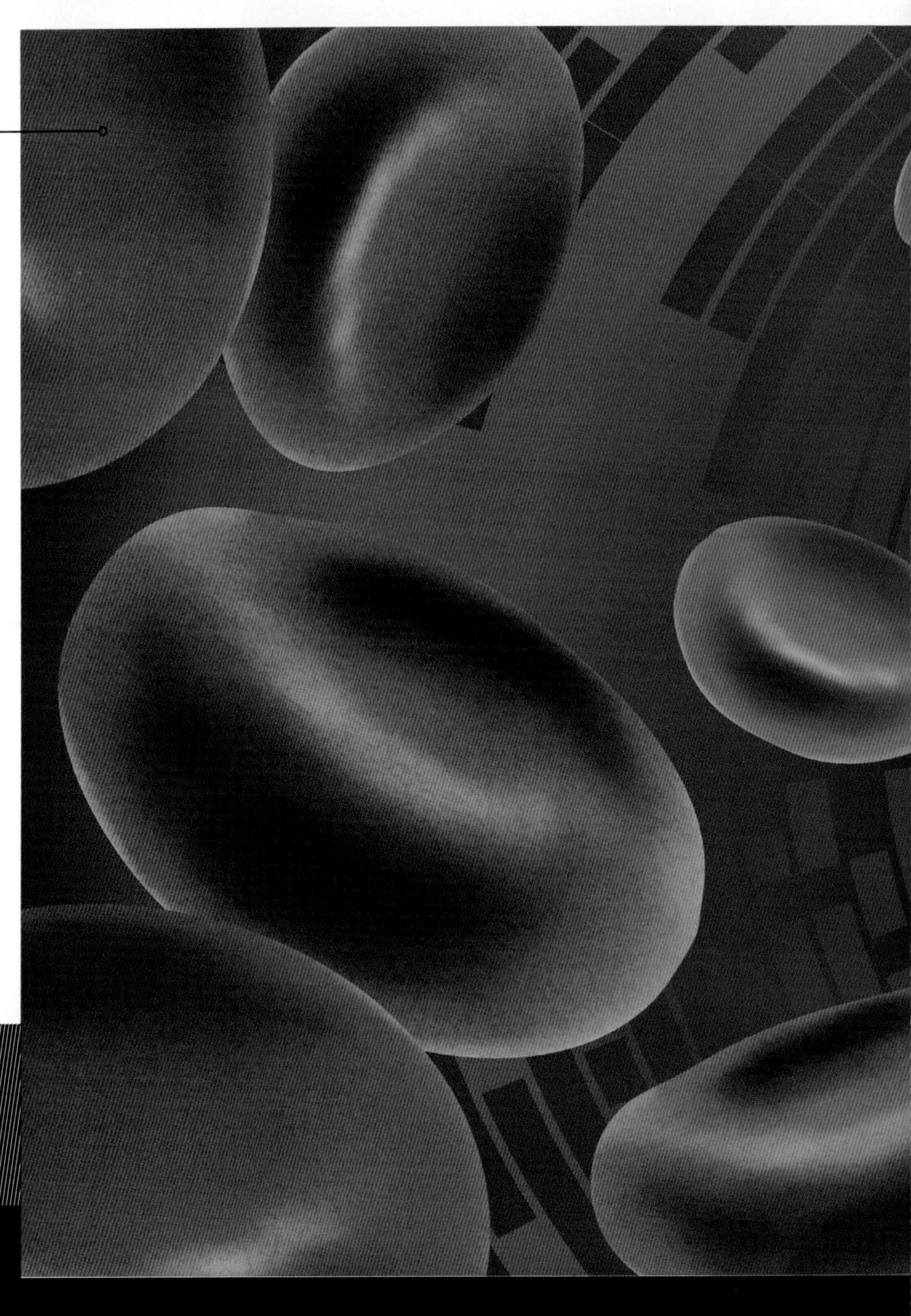

In Japan and South Korea, this is a popular notion, with type A thought to be anxious perfectionists and good team players, type O curious, generous and stubborn, AB arty and unpredictable, and type Bs cheerful, eccentric and selfish. There's no biological reason for this - your blood type is just a question of which surface proteins are attached to your red blood cells - and there is no research to support the idea.

Rather like your astrological star sign, it's possible that knowing what personality type you are 'supposed' to have might cause you to exaggerate or attach extra significance to the occasions when you behave true to type.

This is an example of confirmation bias, where we pay more attention to evidence that appears to support our prejudices than to evidence that contradicts them. Most of us behave with a mixture of all the blood-type personality traits.

WHAT CAUSES HAIR TO TURN GREY?

Going grey is the result of reduced amounts of melanin in the hair, a pigment found in almost all organisms, not just in humans. It is the same compound that tans your skin in response to sunlight. In one form, eumelanin, it results in brown or black hair, while pheomelanin is responsible for red hair and freckles. These are produced in special cells called melanocytes that are found within the hair follicles in the skin. As people get older, their melanocytes become less active and produce less and less melanin, until they finally die and are not replaced. Hairs then grow without any colouring and are transparent. The age at which people turn grey varies widely. Most of the difference is genetic, but other factors such as poor nutrition, smoking and certain diseases can cause premature greying. Even a terrible shock can sometimes cause hair to go grey.

IS HEIGHT MOSTLY DETERMINED BY FATHERS?

No. Adult height is determined by a mixture of genes, diet and hormones. We inherit our genes equally from each parent; indeed, height can be predicted fairly accurately from parents' heights. But we can only grow to our full potential if we have enough good food during childhood and adolescence - and where food is concerned, it may be that mothers have a greater effect.

120

million years is the age of a type of Pterosaur fossil discovered in northeast China. The flying reptile had a wingspan of between 4m and 5m.

WHY WERE PEOPLE SHORTER IN THE PAST?

In the short term, because they were malnourished. In the mid-19th century, the average height of troops was around 5ft 5ins (1.65m) in most European countries, 5ft 6ins (1.68m) in England and over 5ft 7ins (1.70m) in the USA. Men in all these countries are now much taller. Dutchmen were renowned for being short, but now average 6ft (1.83m). Even now, people in impoverished countries are far smaller than in other nations. Yet when they migrate to richer countries, their children grow taller, suggesting the difference is not genetic.

Over longer timespans, the opposite has happened. Fossils show that our ancestors were taller and more muscular than modern people from about 10,000 to 100,000 years ago. After that, skeletons started to become smaller, probably because of agriculture, which drastically reduced people's health. Farming meant an increased population living on a far more restricted diet than hunter-gatherers.

WHY DO WE READ FROM LEFT TO RIGHT AND TOP TO BOTTOM?

It's mainly a matter of convention. Egyptian hieroglyphs could be written in either direction, with the animal and human shapes facing towards the start of the line to show you which way to read it. The advantage of the left-to-right system used in most of the world is that a right-handed person doesn't cover or smudge what they have just written, but there isn't any very good evidence that this is why it is so widely used. Arabic script is still written right-to-left, and Chinese and Japanese can both be written either from left-to-right in horizontal rows, or from top-to-bottom in vertical columns.

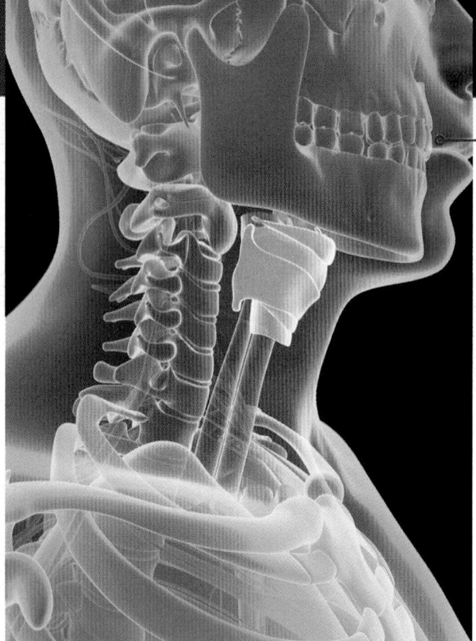

WHY DO OUR VOICES CHANGE AS WE AGE?

For several reasons. During childhood, our voices change gradually as the larynx (voice box) grows larger, making a stronger sound, and the vocal cords mature. Then in boys a dramatic change occurs with puberty as changing hormones affect the size and shape of the larynx and the voice 'breaks'.

Most voices then remain relatively stable for many decades until, in later life, our voice becomes weaker and more tremulous as our muscles begin to shrink, membranes thin, and fine control weakens. Men's voices tend to rise in pitch while women's voices drop. Despite all these changes, though, our own voice can remain recognisable by our family and friends throughout a whole lifetime.

WHAT CAUSES COLOUR BLINDNESS?

Most often it's the lack of one or more of the three types of cone cells, the wavelength-sensitive receptor cells in the retina. These are sometimes called red, green and blue cones, but more accurately are long, medium and short wavelength cones. Most people with normal vision are trichromats and have all three types. Dichromats have only two of the three, usually confusing red and green. Monochromats are far more rare and have only one type. These conditions are inherited, with about one in 20 men and one in 200 women affected. This difference is because the damaged genes are on the X chromosome, and men have only one X chromosome. Women with a functional gene on one of their two X chromosomes are not colourblind.

Not all kinds of colour blindness are genetic. Diseases such as diabetes, Alzheimer's or Parkinson's disease can affect colour vision, as can alcoholism and some medications. Accidents or brain disease can also damage the parts of the brain that process colour.

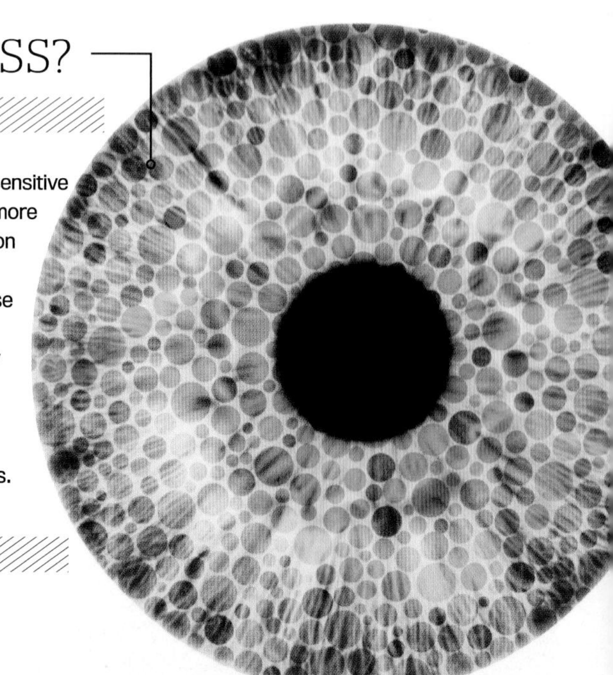

THINKSTOCK X2, GETTY, GETTY IMAGES/SCIENCE PHOTO LIBRARY RM

HOW MANY PEOPLE HAVE EVER LIVED?

The US Population Research Bureau estimates around 107 billion, but this figure involves a lot of assumptions. For one thing, how do you define when humans first began? For another, population records didn't get anywhere close to reliable before 0AD. Even population estimates for the comparatively well-documented Roman Empire can vary by a factor of two. Plagues in Europe during the 14th century and the Byzantine Empire in the 6th century had a huge effect on world population, but there may have been other more ancient catastrophes that we don't know about.

HOW DID SEXUAL REPRODUCTION EVOLVE?

Sexual reproduction is at least 1.2 billion years old, much older than the first appearance of multicellular life on Earth. When these early single-celled organisms reproduced, they simply duplicated their DNA (or RNA, which is a simpler, single-stranded version of DNA) and divided into two identical cells.

This was an efficient way of increasing in number, but because the offspring were clones, it didn't do much to increase variety. Genes could mutate spontaneously over time, but there was no way to quickly bring useful combinations of genes together. Each cell strain had to wait for random mutation to supply all the genes of a particular combination in the same individual at once.

Sexual reproduction shortcuts this by allowing organisms to shuffle their genetic deck of cards. But it may have originally begun as cannibalism: one cell ate another but instead of digesting it completely, the prey DNA became incorporated into the predator cell. If certain genes improved the cellular machinery to make it easier to splice in new genetic sequences, they would be more likely to get carried over as cells ate each other. Eventually this could have evolved into the formation of specialised egg and sperm cells.

Alternatively sex could have begun as a sort of infection. Viruses work by injecting their DNA into a host cell and hijacking the cellular apparatus to make more copies of themselves. If some genes from the ancient host organisms got carried along by the virus when it moved to another host, this could have worked like a primitive form of sperm to share DNA.

WILL HUMANS ALWAYS CONTINUE TO BREAK RECORDS?

The 'purest' Olympic sports, such as running, swimming and jumping, are restricted by our anatomy. The 100m sprint record will probably never drop below nine seconds, because the forces required would rip your tendons from your bones and evolution is unlikely to change our bodies enough to bypass these limits. But Paralympians with ever more sophisticated 'bionic' legs will probably break able-bodied records one day, while new sports will no doubt be invented with new records for us to break.

THINKSTOCK, AP/PRESS ASSOCIATION, ALAMY, SCIENCE PHOTO LIBRARY, GETTY X4 (THE LIFE IMAGES COLLECTION, AFP, THE ASAHI SHIMBUN X2)

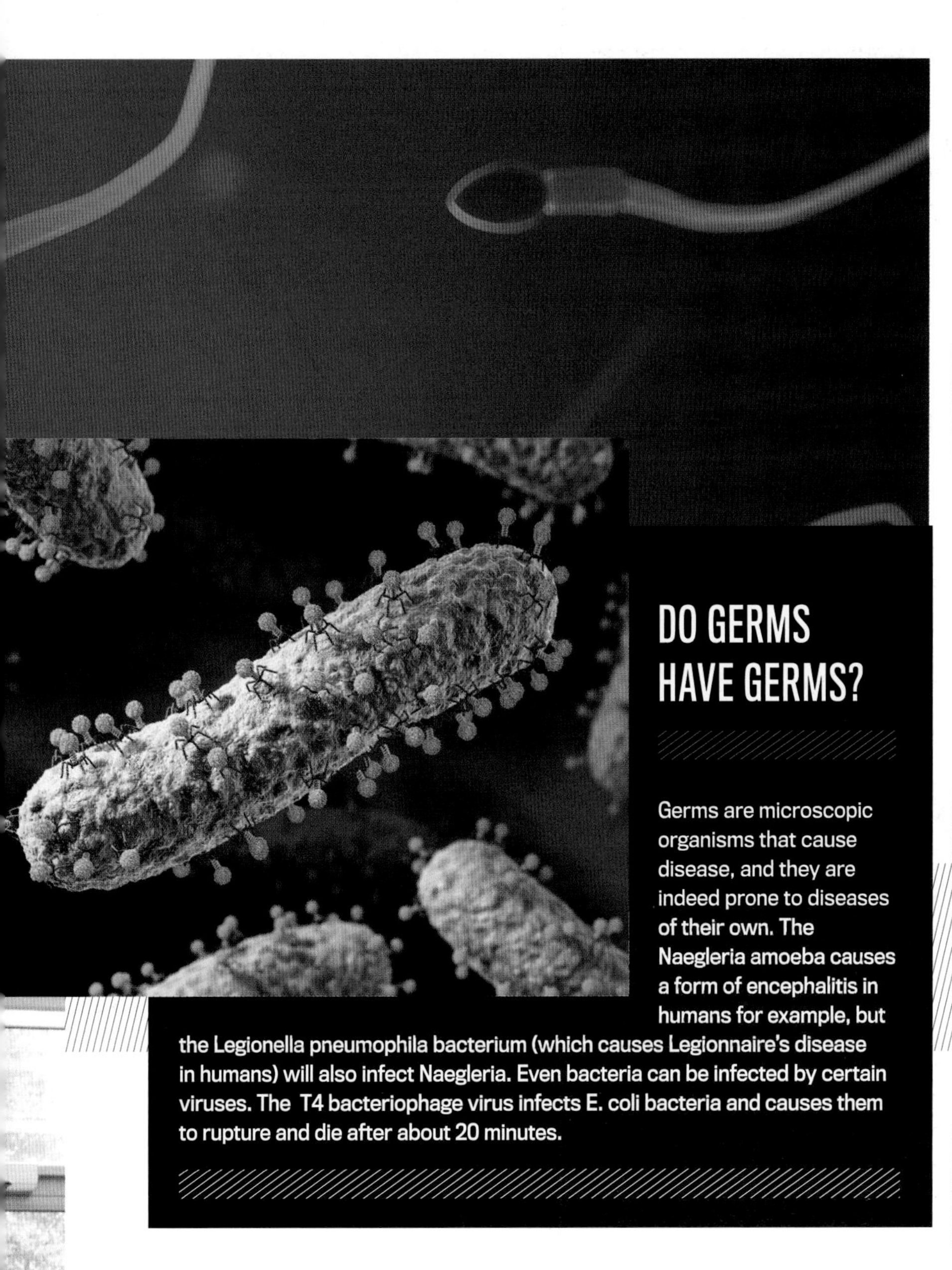

DO GERMS HAVE GERMS?

Germs are microscopic organisms that cause disease, and they are indeed prone to diseases of their own. The Naegleria amoeba causes a form of encephalitis in humans for example, but the Legionella pneumophila bacterium (which causes Legionnaire's disease in humans) will also infect Naegleria. Even bacteria can be infected by certain viruses. The T4 bacteriophage virus infects E. coli bacteria and causes them to rupture and die after about 20 minutes.

COULD A NEANDERTHAL BE CLONED?

Yes, in principle. In May 2010, a draft sequence of the Neanderthal genome was published in the journal *Science*, based on the analysis of fragments of DNA that had previously been recovered from 38,000-year-old bones found in Croatia. The international team, led by scientists at the Max Planck Institute in Germany, used a sequencing machine to obtain short stretches of DNA code that were then stitched together by computers. Currently, the sequence only covers around 60 percent of the entire genome. But, once complete, it could be used to create an artificial genome.

However, this would be useless unless the DNA could be packaged into chromosomes inside a living cell, enabling the genes to be correctly expressed. Alternatively, the DNA of a living human cell could be altered using a nuclear transfer process, as has been done when cloning goats and cows. Finally, it might be possible to grow Neanderthal stem cells which could then be implanted into the very early stage of a human embryo. All non-Neanderthal cells would then be removed, allowing a Neanderthal baby to grow.

So it could be done, but should we do it? The result might be physically Neanderthal but this creature would not be born into a Neanderthal society or environment and so would not be adapted to today's diseases, let alone to modern life.

What is this?

Each bright spot in this picture is a bolt of lightning that struck Earth over a 15-minute period. Taken from the International Space Station by astronaut Don Pettit, this time-lapse photograph is made up of multiple 30-second exposures. They were brought together using image processing software. Stars appear as bright trails across the deep blue of the night sky, while city lights streak across Earth.

Only when looking from space do you notice quite how many thunderstorms are going on. "There are roughly four million lightning flashes per day spread over the planet," says Professor Joseph Dwyer, a lightning scientist at the Florida Institute of Technology. The flash rate changes over the course of the day, peaking when the Sun is over large land masses, such as Africa and the Americas.

For more great pictures, follow us on http://pinterest.com/sciencefocus

NASA/JSC

TECHNOLOGY

The fast-paced world of technology is constantly changing and adapting, with gadgets becoming outdated as soon as new models are brought onto the market. But how do they all work?

HOW ARE SAT-NAV VOICES PROGRAMMED?

Initially, voices on sat-nav and other talking gadgets were synthesised. But actors and celebrities have now lent their voices to the devices to replace the robotic ones. In some systems, the actor is recorded saying all likely words and phrases. Each recording is turned into an audio file that's triggered by the software on the machine. But that only works if the range of possible voice prompts is quite limited. More elaborate systems record dozens or even hundreds of individual sounds, or phonemes. These are digitally stitched together to form coherent words, having been processed to reproduce the correct intonation, duration and emphasis.

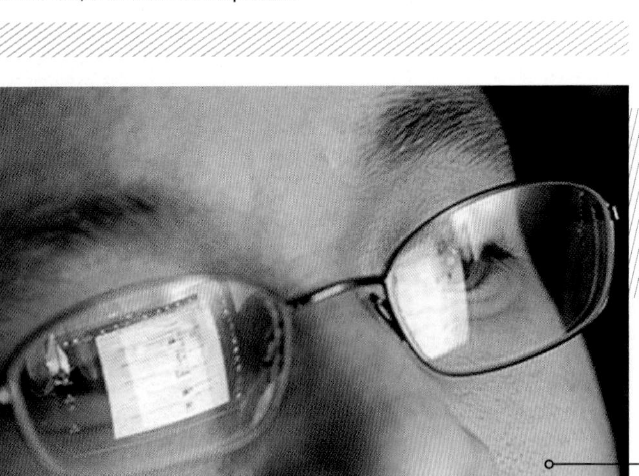

WHY DO COMPUTERS MAKE OUR EYES TIRED?

Eye-strain comes from a combination of screen flicker and the effects of frequently shifting your gaze around different parts of the screen. A computer display is usually wider than a book, making it harder work on the eyes. Also, unlike a printed page where dark letters are printed on a light background, the screen itself emits light. The brightness of the display can therefore make your eyes tired too, especially if there is glare or if you are working in a poorly lit room.

HOW DO BANK CARD READERS WORK?

Bank card readers used to work similarly to the heads in a tape machine. Information was transferred as the card's magnetic strip passed over the reader. In chip-and-pin devices, the readers make electrical contact with an embedded chip on the card. Like the magnetic strip, the user's PIN is encrypted on the chip. When the correct number is entered, the card authorises the payment.

SUPERSTOCK, ALAMY, THINKSTOCK X2

HOW HIGH WILL SKYSCRAPERS GO IN THE FUTURE?

The current tallest building in the world is the Burj Khalifa in Dubai (pictured). At 828m, it is nearly three times higher than the Shard London Bridge. The 443m Empire State Building was once the world's tallest, but is little more than half the height of the Burj Khalifa. It seems we can just keep going taller, especially as exotic, super-strong lightweight materials like nano-enhanced concrete become more affordable.

But one limit is a building's footprint. Already, the bases of skyscrapers take up nearly as much space as a New York City block. The other issue is elevators. The fastest can manage 17m per second. Non-stop, that's nearly a minute to scale a 1,000m tower. To reach the top of a 4km-high building would therefore take a full four minutes! But architects at the Japanese company Taisei have conceived of just such a tall building. The X-Seed 4000 is simply a proof of principle for now. It's unlikely to be built, requiring a 6km-wide base located in the sea.

HOW DOES MY MOBILE KNOW I'M ABROAD?

When you get off the plane, your phone connects with the host network. The visited provider notes that you are not registered with it and connects to your home provider through the phone's international mobile subscriber identity number. Once the networks are talking to each other, the foreign provider finds out whether your contract allows roaming.

HOW POWERFUL WOULD A COMPUTER HAVE TO BE TO MATCH HUMAN CONSCIOUSNESS?

Philosophers and scientists have proposed many tests for machine consciousness. One is being able to perceive voices – but the iPhone personal assistant Siri uses voice recognition and nobody would argue that is conscious. A machine passes the Turing Test if a user is unable to distinguish between interacting with it and a human. But even that is some way from saying the computer has self-awareness or emotions. Views vary, but no amount of computation is sufficient for 'strong' artificial consciousness, whereby a machine has feelings, is self-aware and is capable of abstract reasoning. But if an appearance of sentience is sufficient, all it takes is one of the many chatbots available online.

WHY DOES STANDING NEAR A RADIO IMPROVE RECEPTION?

In an area with poor reception, a radio struggles to separate the useful signal from the electromagnetic noise. Between the radio and the distant transmitter, radio waves become scattered, bouncing off surfaces and being absorbed by buildings and terrain on the way. Your body also absorbs radio waves and affects their pattern as they arrive at the aerial. As you move around, the pattern shifts through constructive and destructive interference, causing the reception to fluctuate. Touching the receiver usually helps the reception, because absorbing all those waves makes you a surprisingly effective antennae.

HOW DO COMPUTERISED FIREWORK DISPLAYS WORK?

In a computerised firework display, the pyrotechnics are detonated by electric matches, or e-matches. The e-match head contains a zirconium compound that ignites readily when heated, the heat coming from a coil of wire encasing the head. The e-matches are triggered remotely from controllers called electronic firing panels, which have banks of switches assigned either to individual pyrotechnics or batches to be fired simultaneously. The more advanced panels run automatically from computer code. This is often programmed using specialist pyrotechnic software and then downloaded to the panel before the display. Using software to launch a display is open to error, however, as seen at the San Diego 2012 Fourth of July celebrations when a glitch triggered all the fireworks at once.

DID YOU KNOW?

In 2012, a hospital in Northern Ireland became the first in the UK to use a telepresence robot. Dr Charles McAllister used the robot at Daisy Hill Hospital to interact with patients 32km away.

WHAT ARE BYTES USED TO MEASURE?

A byte is made up of eight bits, each representing either a one or zero. Two bits can carry up to four values (00, 01, 10 or 11); three bits offer eight values and so on up to 8 bits, with 256 possible combinations. Each character in a document is a byte. That gives enough values for all the letters in upper and lower case, all the numbers, punctuation and many other symbols.

IS LASER PROPULSION POSSIBLE?

Using intense laser beams as a form of propulsion is possible; in fact, it's being investigated as a means of powering everything from aircraft to small satellites and even interstellar spacecraft. In the 1960s, the pioneering Austrian aerospace engineer Eugen Sänger sketched out the most direct form of laser propulsion: using the blast of radiation pressure from laser light to push vehicles through space. Unfortunately, its simplicity comes at the cost of requiring incredibly intense laser beams that are impractical using current technology. This has led researchers to focus on the more attainable goal of using lasers to blast material off a metal propellant, producing thrust acting in the opposite direction. During the 1970s, experiments in the UK and US suggested this might be capable of launching small payloads into orbit at just one per cent of the cost of using conventional rockets.

So far, however, the only real-life use of lasers in propulsion is for powering small drones remotely, where laser beams are used to transmit light energy to photocells on the aircraft. Experiments by NASA scientists in 2002 proved the concept and it's now being developed for use with small helicopter-like devices.

HOW DO BULLETPROOF VESTS WORK?

Bulletproof vests are designed to disperse the round's energy and deform the slug to minimise blunt force trauma. Hard body armour is made of strengthened steel plates; strong and effective, it's also heavy and cumbersome. But some ammunition can even penetrate steel, requiring stronger materials still.

The latest vests employ overlapping super-strength but lightweight composites of ceramic and titanium. Soft body armour is not as strong, but it is more lightweight and less conspicuous to wear. It is woven out of interlacing strands of Kevlar. Like hard body armour, layers of this tough, net-like material deform the incoming bullet, robbing it of its energy.

WHAT ARE ANALOGUE TV SIGNALS USED FOR NOW?

Analogue TV broadcasts ceased in October 2012, freeing up spectrum around the 800MHz band. Ofcom is auctioning off the bandwidth to 4G mobile service providers. The 800Mhz spectrum is close to that of digital terrestrial TV, causing concerns that mobile base stations will interfere with set-top boxes. But mobile providers have set up an alliance called Digital Mobile Spectrum to monitor and limit the impact on television services.

IS SHORTWAVE RADIO STILL IN USE?

Yes it is. For example, the BBC World Service still broadcasts in shortwave from the Ascension Island relay in the Atlantic off the coast of West Africa. The shortwave band is from around 3MHz-20MHz. At these frequencies, the signals bounce off the Earth's upper atmosphere, meaning that a single transmitter can cover areas thousands of kilometres across. Other BBC shortwave stations cover more of Africa, as well as large regions of Asia, Middle East and Gulf states, Afghanistan and Iran.

HOW DO INFRARED TV CONTROLS WORK?

Infrared remotes send a binary signal encoded with a command. Instructions to change the channel or adjust the volume are usually encoded in a seven-bit code. Added to that is a device identifier so that the commands acts on the television rather than, say, your set-top box. The command is converted into the invisible flashing of your remote's LED in one of three ways: pulse, space or shift-coded. In the former, the duration of the light pulse represents the binary bit. For instance, a longer pulse could be a '1' and a short pulse, a '0'. Space-coded is the same, only the space between pulses carries the binary bits. Shift-coded is where the television detects what the pulse is doing at regular intervals in time. The LED going from off to on during one of those intervals, or on to off, carries the desired bit of code.

ARE MOBILE PHONE SIGNALS STRONGER IN HOT WEATHER?

Temperature has no significant effect on mobile signals. But moisture can attenuate radio waves through the air slightly. In other words, it can absorb the signals and weaken them, so you may have marginally poorer reception in heavy rain or high humidity. Mobile phone signals are in the microwave band at a wavelength of about 15 to 30cm, in a radio frequency sweet spot where atmospheric attenuation is at a minimum. However, water molecules absorb a small amount of energy even in this band. Radio waves are also affected by electrical storms when air molecules become ionised. So if hot weather triggers thunderstorms, it can disrupt phone signals in this way.

Other factors that can affect mobiles and indeed all communications are those from beyond our world. Space weather, caused by phenomena such as solar flares, causes streams of charged particles to breach the magnetosphere, bombarding the communications infrastructure and disrupting mobile phone traffic.

HOW DO COMPUTER VIRUSES WORK?

Some viruses attack the computer's boot sector, the area on the hard drive that hosts the code for the start-up routine. Such a root code virus causes havoc because it runs itself every time you switch on the computer. Other viruses are hidden in emails, games or attached documents. These applications will appear to run normally but in the background; the malign code plays tricks like sending infected emails to everyone in your contacts list.

Another kind of malicious agent is the worm. This is able to replicate itself, often programming the infected machine to send copies to myriad random computers. Successful worms spread almost exponentially through networks, consuming processing power and bandwidth as they go.

But some of the most widespread disruption comes from botnets. Malicious code, often spread through email attachments, installs itself on thousands of computers. The hijacked machines act as an unwitting army of zombies firing off spam emails or blitzing targets like defence or corporate mainframes. They overwhelm them with a barrage of requests for information in so-called distributed denial of service attacks.

HOW DOES A MICROPHONE PICK UP SOUNDS?

A microphone converts sound into a small electrical current. Sound waves hit a diaphragm that vibrates, moving a magnet near a coil. In some designs, the coil moves within a magnet.

Other microphones, for example condenser microphones, work on the principle of capacitance. Capacitors consist of parallel conducting plates that store charge and are used to smooth out signals like voltage variations in a power supply. In a condenser microphone, the incoming sound vibrates one plate of a capacitor. The varying capacitance is converted into a corresponding electrical signal.

ARE DIGITAL CLOCKS MORE ACCURATE THAN ANALOGUE CLOCKS?

In fact, analogue clocks are more precise than digital ones, but they are not necessarily more accurate. That might seem contradictory, but the sweep of the hands on an analogue clock is continuous, whereas a digital clock is governed by fixed values. Therefore, an analogue clock can show a precise time. A digital timekeeper approximates to an interval determined by the number of digits on its display. So it can be more accurate, but less precise.

1.4

terabits per second is the speed of the fastest broadband connection ever, achieved in London in 2014. This is enough to download 44 uncompressed HD films a second!

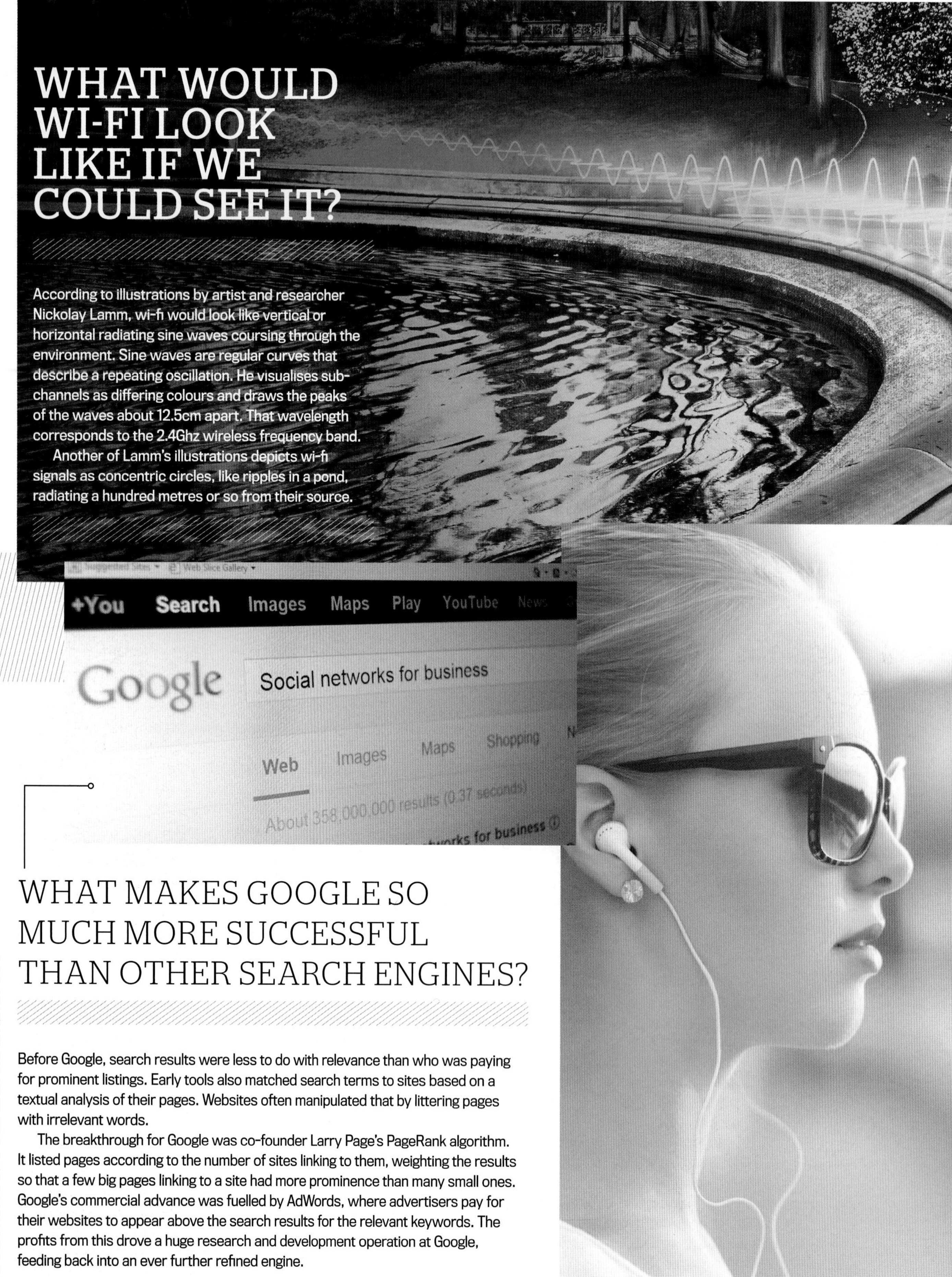

WHAT WOULD WI-FI LOOK LIKE IF WE COULD SEE IT?

According to illustrations by artist and researcher Nickolay Lamm, wi-fi would look like vertical or horizontal radiating sine waves coursing through the environment. Sine waves are regular curves that describe a repeating oscillation. He visualises sub-channels as differing colours and draws the peaks of the waves about 12.5cm apart. That wavelength corresponds to the 2.4Ghz wireless frequency band.

Another of Lamm's illustrations depicts wi-fi signals as concentric circles, like ripples in a pond, radiating a hundred metres or so from their source.

WHAT MAKES GOOGLE SO MUCH MORE SUCCESSFUL THAN OTHER SEARCH ENGINES?

Before Google, search results were less to do with relevance than who was paying for prominent listings. Early tools also matched search terms to sites based on a textual analysis of their pages. Websites often manipulated that by littering pages with irrelevant words.

The breakthrough for Google was co-founder Larry Page's PageRank algorithm. It listed pages according to the number of sites linking to them, weighting the results so that a few big pages linking to a site had more prominence than many small ones. Google's commercial advance was fuelled by AdWords, where advertisers pay for their websites to appear above the search results for the relevant keywords. The profits from this drove a huge research and development operation at Google, feeding back into an ever further refined engine.

NICKOLAY LAMM/MYDEALS.COM/REX, ALAMY X5, THINKSTOCK, AFP/GETTY IMAGES

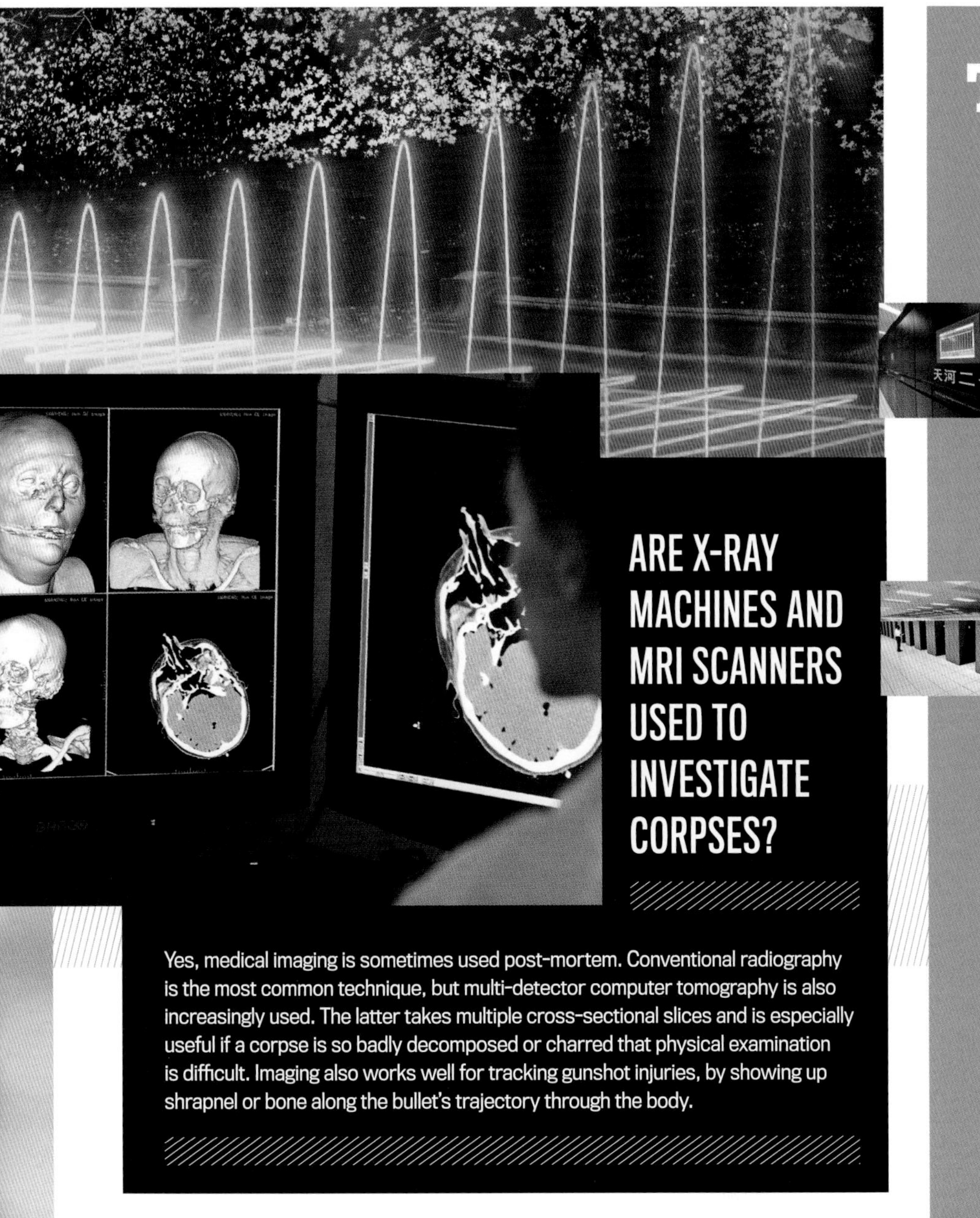

ARE X-RAY MACHINES AND MRI SCANNERS USED TO INVESTIGATE CORPSES?

Yes, medical imaging is sometimes used post-mortem. Conventional radiography is the most common technique, but multi-detector computer tomography is also increasingly used. The latter takes multiple cross-sectional slices and is especially useful if a corpse is so badly decomposed or charred that physical examination is difficult. Imaging also works well for tracking gunshot injuries, by showing up shrapnel or bone along the bullet's trajectory through the body.

ARE EARPHONES REALLY DAMAGING TO HEALTH?

Doctors have long warned of the damaging effects of prolonged exposure to loud music via earphones. The popularity of portable cassette players in the 1980s led to studies claiming that around one in 20 people were risking Noise-Induced Hearing Loss.

Yet while there is no doubt that exposure to loud noise from, for example, machinery can lead to permanent damage, evidence that music from portable devices does the same has remained elusive. That's changing, however, as scientists focus on finding actual physical damage to nerves. Dr Martine Hamann and colleagues at the University of Leicester recently published the first evidence of such harm, showing that loud noises strip nerve cells of their protective coating, preventing them from reliably transmitting signals from the ear to the brain.

This confirms what previous studies have shown – that even brief exposure to loud music can reduce the sensitivity of the ear. But the finding also explains why evidence of permanent damage has been elusive. Dr Hamann found that nerve cells repair themselves, replacing the outer layer after a few months – if they're given the chance.

TOP TEN

MOST POWERFUL COMPUTERS

Assessed using Linpack benchmark by Top 100 Supercomputer Sites (top500.org) in November 2013

1. Tianhe-2 (Milky Way-2)
Where: National Super Computer Center, Guangzhou, China
Rmax: 33.86 petaflops

2. Titan
Where: DOE/SC/Oak Ridge National Laboratory, USA
Rmax: 17.59 petaflops

3. Sequoia
Where: DOE/NNSA/Lawrence Livermore National Laboratory, USA
Rmax: 17.17 petaflops

4. K Computer
Where: RIKEN Advanced Institute for Computational Science, (AICS), Japan
Rmax: 10.51 petaflops

5. Mira
Where: DOE/SC/Argonne National Laboratory, USA
Rmax: 8.59 petaflops

6. Piz Daint
Where: Swiss National Supercomputing Centre (CSCS), Switzerland
Rmax: 6.27 petaflops

7. Stampede
Where: Texas Advanced Computing Center/ University of Texas, USA
Rmax: 5.17 petaflops

8. JUQUEEN
Where: Forschungszentrum Juelich (FZJ), Germany
Rmax: 5.01 petaflops

9. Vulcan
Where: DOE/NNSA/Lawrence Livermore National Laboratory, USA
Rmax: 4.29 petaflops

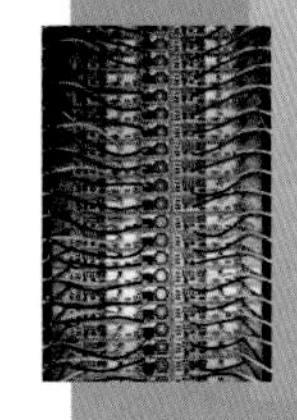

10. SuperMUC
Where: Leibniz Rechenzentrum, Germany
Rmax: 2.90 petaflops

How did these rocks get their stripes?

The striking lines running through the hills of the Zhangye Danxia Landform Geological Park in China look like they've been painted on. But this remarkable landscape tells the story of 20 million years' worth of geological activity.

"This area would have once been a lake," says Professor John Underhill, an expert in stratigraphy at the University of Edinburgh. "During colder, wetter climes, the lake would have been full and iron would have been deposited into the sediment, creating the red banding. During hotter periods, the lake would dry up and the iron would have been leached from the ground leaving behind the white bands."

You would normally only see this visual record of the country's fluctuating climate by drilling into the ground, but these beds have been lifted up and tilted by tectonic processes. More recently, rainfall and water drainage has sculpted the exposed landscape into the sharp peaks and valleys seen today.

For more great pictures, follow us on http://pinterest.com/sciencefocus

AMOS CHAPPLE/REX FEATURES

MATHS & PHYSICS

Uncovering the solutions to all the big questions has always driven the leading minds of our planet. And the answers certainly make for a fascinating read...

HOW DO ONE-WAY MIRRORS WORK?

A one-way mirror allows people in one room to observe another via a window coated with a thin layer of reflective material. The trick lies in making this layer thin enough to see through, but thick enough to bounce back any bright light striking it. Then, by keeping the room under observation much brighter than the other, it's possible to look into it without being seen.

CAN YOU MAKE MONEY BY ALWAYS BETTING ON FAVOURITES?

It seems obvious that the horse or football team with the shortest odds has the best chance of winning, and is thus the best bet. The trouble is that favourites don't always win. In fact, in the 144,000 horse races that ran in the UK between 1991 and 2010, the favourite won just 34 per cent of the time.

That wouldn't be a problem if the odds being offered were good enough to compensate for those losses. But they're not: typically they're less than evens so, in the long run, the money you make when favourites win is outweighed by the amount you lose when they don't. If you'd put £1 on every favourite over those 20 years, you'd have ended up losing around £12,000.

ALAMY X2, THINKSTOCK X2

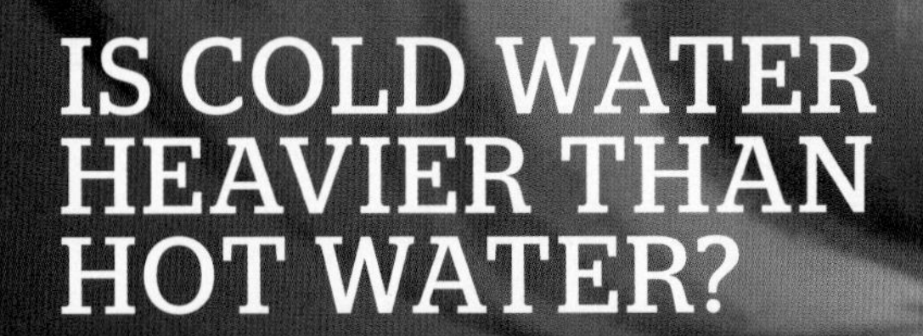

IS COLD WATER HEAVIER THAN HOT WATER?

No. Cold water is denser than hot water (for temperatures above 4°C) because the individual molecules move more slowly and thus pack together more tightly. So a litre of water at 4°C weighs about 4.3 per cent more than a litre of water at just below boiling point. But that's because to fill a litre bottle with water at 4°C, you need to add more molecules of water than you do when the water is at 100°C. A greater number of molecules weighs more than a lesser number.

But if you take a sealed litre bottle of water at 100°C and let it cool to 4°C, without losing or gaining any molecules, you'd expect it to weigh the same. The really surprising thing, however, is that the mass actually drops. That's because Einstein's famous equation, $E = mc^2$, means that mass and energy are really the same thing. So you can't remove energy from a system without also taking some of its mass. When the water cools, it loses energy and therefore mass, and the surrounding air gains energy/mass by the same amount. The effect is very small though. For each °C that the litre of water cools, it loses 4.7×10^{-14}kg. That's about the weight of two human sperm cells.

WHAT'S THE BEST PAINKILLER?

When experiencing a bad headache or other acute pain, most people reach for tablets of the 'big three' over-the-counter painkillers: aspirin, paracetamol or ibuprofen. But which one works best? A study by a team led by Dr Andrew Moore of the Pain Research Unit at the Churchill Hospital in Oxford found that aspirin only works well in around 35-40 per cent of people, compared to 45 per cent of those taking paracetamol and 55 per cent for ibuprofen. The proportions for all these increase by around 5 to 10 percentage points if 100mg of caffeine are added. According to Dr Moore, the best results come from a combination of 500mg of paracetamol, 200mg of ibuprofen plus a strong cup of coffee. He cautions, however, that anyone with recurrent pain should see their GP.

WHAT WOULD HAPPEN IF YOU DROPPED A BOMB ON A VOLCANO?

When Mount St Helens erupted in Washington State, in 1980, the initial blast was equivalent to around seven megatons of TNT. That's broadly equivalent to the yield of modern thermonuclear weapons. But the explosion that blows the top off a volcano is only a small part of the total energy released during the eruption. If you dropped a nuclear bomb into the crater of an extinct volcano, you would flatten the mountain out a bit but you wouldn't set the volcano off because there wouldn't be any pre-existing upwelling of magma. On an already active volcano, or one that is just about to blow, a nuclear bomb might alter the lava flow, or cause it to erupt a little sooner.

The US army and Air Force have conducted trials with conventional bombs in Hawaii, to try and block or divert the course of individual lava forms, on numerous occasions since 1935. The results have been mixed at best. Lava is heavy, hot and very determined.

IS IT MORE EFFICIENT TO PUSH OR PULL A GOLF TROLLEY?

As long ago as 1973, research at the University of Texas found that the human skeleton exerts the most pushing force when your hands are at 70 per cent of your shoulder height from the floor, which is roughly chest height. When you are pulling, however, this changes to 40 per cent of shoulder height, or between the hip and knee. Three- and four-wheel trolleys stay upright and the handle is too high for efficient pulling, so you should push them. But the traditional, two-wheeled golf trolley tilts up when you roll it, so the height of the handle is much closer to the ideal pulling height. Pulling a trolley also saves some energy in steering, because the wheels are behind the towing point, so it automatically follows you. When you push a trolley, you'll need to exert some extra force at the wrist as you continually adjust its course.

WHY IS THE SPEED OF LIGHT CONSTANT?

It isn't. When it passes through some mediums, such as water, it slows down considerably. In the case of diamond, its speed is cut by over 50 per cent. But according to Einstein's Special Theory of Relativity, the speed of light in the vacuum of empty space is said to be the same for all observers, at just short of 300,000km/s.

This is undoubtedly weird, as every other speed is measured relative to something else. For example, a train can move at 150km/h relative to someone on a platform, but to the train's passengers its speed is pretty much zero. The speed of light is no ordinary speed, however: it's a universal constant that emerges from the laws of physics.

Specifically, it's the speed at which electromagnetic waves travel through the vacuum of space – and its value can be predicted by equations unifying our understanding of electricity and magnetism, as discovered over 150 years ago by the Scottish physicist and mathematician James Clerk Maxwell.

WHAT MAKES SOMETHING TRANSPARENT?

Whether a substance is transparent depends on how light interacts with its atoms. If they're of the right frequency, an atom's electrons can absorb photons of light, making the matter opaque. However, the atoms of transparent matter enable photons to pass through.

HOW DO WE KNOW THE LAWS OF PHYSICS APPLY THROUGHOUT THE UNIVERSE?

To be blunt, we don't - it's just an assumption. Science proceeds by constructing theories on the basis of plausible principles, such as Einstein's assertion that the laws of physics must be the same regardless of how fast one travels. These are then put to observational test and are modified when they prove unreliable.

CAN SCIENCE EXPLAIN LUCK?

If you throw a die and it falls down, that's not luck, that's gravity. But calculating exactly which number ends face up requires you to know all the forces involved, the movement of the air molecules and so on. That's much too hard to do in the time it takes for the die to land, so we commonly say that it's down to 'chance'. This means that there are too many parameters to figure out the outcome of the event in the given time, or we can't calculate them accurately enough.

'Luck' is the word we use to describe the particular outcome of a chance event. If a die rolls a six, we might call it good luck; if it rolls a one, we might call it bad luck. But if every number has the same probability of rolling, then 'luck' is just a story we tell ourselves to make sense of the event retrospectively.

Humans are story-telling animals. We look at the world as a narrative, usually with ourselves at its centre. The science of psychology has something to say about why we find luck such an attractive concept, and maths can explain why some random events happen more often than we intuitively feel they should. But physics can't explain luck itself, because it is a fiction of our own making.

HOW ARE NUTRITIONAL VALUES DETERMINED?

Calorie content is measured in a device called a bomb calorimeter. You burn a sample in a sealed container of pure oxygen immersed in water, and measure how much the water temperature rises. For protein measurement, the Kjeldahl method uses sulphuric acid to react with the nitrogen in protein and measures how much ammonia is produced. Fats can be measured by dissolving them out in a solvent, such as hexane.

500

trillion watts was the power of the most intense laser shot ever fired, as part of experiments into fusion energy at the National Ignition Facility in the US on 5 July 2012.

WHAT'S THE MAXIMUM GRADIENT A CYCLIST CAN CLIMB?

With enough run-up, you can ride up any gradient of hill, including completely vertical. But beginning from a standing start, the limiting factor is the power you can supply from your legs. Most cyclists can't balance once they are travelling at less than 1m/s. An Olympic athlete can put out about 370-400 watts of power for short periods and this would theoretically let them climb at 1m/s up a roughly 45 per cent grade hill, ignoring friction from the bike axles.

There aren't any roads with hills that steep, but one of the steepest in the world is Baldwin Street in Dunedin, New Zealand (pictured). This has a maximum grade of about 35 per cent and there are videos on YouTube of cyclists making it to the top. They invariably zig-zag on the way up though, which flattens the effective gradient.

IS IT POSSIBLE TO BUILD IMMUNITY TO ELECTRIC SHOCKS?

An electric shock is just another kind of stimulus and if you are regularly exposed to the same stimulus, your nervous system will eventually respond less strongly to it. But this desensitisation only really applies to mild stimuli. You can't 'train' yourself starting with mild shocks and eventually work up to the point where you can safely stick your fingers in a 13-amp socket.

CAN FINANCIAL CRASHES BE PREDICTED?

Financial crashes occur when investors suddenly decide prices are too divorced from the true value of some asset. Over the centuries, crashes have taken place in everything from stock markets to the price of tulips. With even Isaac Newton losing a fortune by failing to spot a market crash in 1720, it's clear that predicting them is far from simple.

Even so, a team led by Prof Didier Sornette at the Swiss Federal Institute of Technology claims to have found a tell-tale sign. They look for a wave-like pattern in the rising price of the asset, whose peaks get closer together according to a certain rule. Prof Sornette and his colleagues have used this so-called log-normal periodicity to predict some famous crashes, including the 2008 global financial crisis.

THINKSTOCK X2, GETTY IMAGES, CLAUS ABLEITER

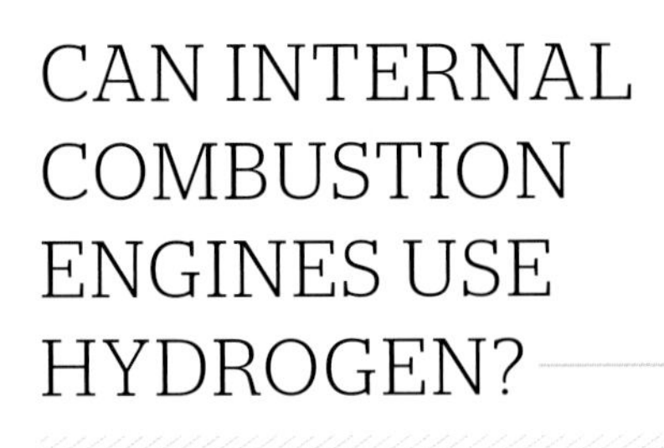

CAN INTERNAL COMBUSTION ENGINES USE HYDROGEN?

The idea of using hydrogen gas in car engines actually pre-dates the use of petrol, with the first such engine being built over 200 years ago. It wasn't a success and hydrogen remains challenging to use, because of its lightness and flammability. This makes it hard to transport and ignition hard to control.

DID YOU KNOW?

On 8 March 2011, Jayasimha Ravirala of India memorised a 264-digit binary number in one minute - a world record. Ravirala currently holds 13 Guinness World Records.

WHAT ARE THE CHANCES OF TWO SNOOKER GAMES BEING IDENTICAL?

Very slim indeed, because snooker involves so-called chaotic processes in which just small changes produce radically different outcomes. Rough calculations shows that if two snooker games are played with the first red ball struck to within a hair's breadth of the exact same position, the games will be hugely different after around half a dozen shots.

TOP TEN
MOST EXPENSIVE EXPERIMENTS

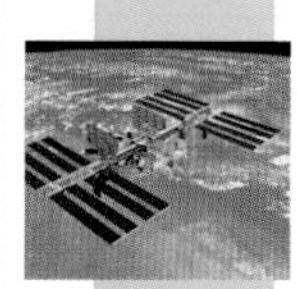

1. International Space Station
Cost: $150bn (£92bn)
The ISS has been continuously occupied by astronauts since 2 November 2000.

2. International Thermonuclear Experimental Reactor
Cost: $20.6bn (£12.3bn)
Construction began in 2010 on what will become the world's largest tokamak fusion device.

3. James Webb Space Telescope
Cost: $8bn (£4.9bn)
Scheduled to launch in 2018, this telescope will investigate how galaxies form.

4. International Linear Collider
Cost: $6.65bn (£4.1bn)
Construction is due to begin in 2016 for this particle accelerator.

5. Large Hadron Collider
Cost: $6.4bn (£3.84bn)
Currently the world's largest and highest-energy particle accelerator.

6. Cassini-Huygens Spacecraft
Cost: $3.26bn (£2bn)
Launched in 1997, the Huygens lander probe separated in 2004 to investigate Saturn's largest moon, Titan.

7. Envisat
Cost: $3.1bn (£1.9bn)
Envisat spent 10 years in orbit mentoring signs of environmental impact and climate change on Earth's atmosphere.

8. Human Genome Project
Cost: $2.7bn (£1.65bn)
Started in 1990, this project lasted 13 years and mapped the entire human genome.

9. Curiosity Rover
Cost: $2.5bn (£1.5bn)
This robotic rover was designed to investigate whether life could ever have existed on Mars.

10. Super-conducting Super Collider
Cost: $2bn (£1.2bn)
Construction on the particle accelerator was stopped in 1983 – but not until nearly half the budget had been spent.

WHY DOES LIGHT MAKE THINGS FADE?

Sunlight is a mixture of different wavelengths of light. The shorter the wavelength, the more energy the photons carry. Wavelengths shorter than about 400nm (the ultra violet range) have enough energy to break the chemical bonds in some compounds. Pigments from natural dyes tend to be quite large molecules with lots of fairly weak bonds. Red pigments fade more readily because they only reflect the lower energy red wavelengths and absorb everything else, increasing the chance of molecular damage. Glass absorbs a lot of the ultra violet, but objects left on a window ledge will still fade over time.

HOW DO WE KNOW THAT PI IS INFINITE?

Many people know that the value of Pi is roughly 22 divided by seven, which is around 99.96 per cent accurate – plenty good enough for most practical purposes. But in 1768, the Swiss mathematician Johann Lambert revealed the remarkable fact that it's impossible to use any such fractions to pin down the precise value of Pi as it just goes on forever.

To prove it, he showed that Pi is not a 'rational' number – that is one the exact value of which is given by the ratio of two whole numbers. Rational numbers can be turned into decimal numbers that either stop after a few places (like 1/8 = 0.125) or just keep repeating after a certain number of places (such as 4/7 = 0.571428571... and so on). By showing that Pi is not a rational number, Lambert revealed that its decimal value neither stops nor cycles – but just carries on to infinity.

ALAMY X2, THINKSTOCK X3, NASA

WHAT DOES A SHEET OF GRAPHENE LOOK LIKE?

Graphene is made up of hexagonal patterns of carbon atoms, rather like chicken wire. Tiny sheets of the stuff can be created simply by applying sticky tape to slivers of graphite and peeling it off. But being only one atomic layer in thickness, the layer has to be stuck to special film in order to be seen.

IS IT BETTER TO PLAY THE SAME LOTTERY NUMBERS?

The chances of winning the jackpot remain one in 14 million whether you stick with the same numbers or take the 'lucky dip' option, which uses a randomiser to create fresh numbers each time. But the lucky dip does stop you using common selections and thus having to share the prize with many others.

WHAT ARE SUBATOMIC PARTICLES MADE OF?

We're used to describing objects as made from certain chemicals, which in turn are made of specific atoms and finally subatomic particles. Many theorists think these ultimate components are themselves a form of energy created by the vibrations of bizarre multidimensional entities called superstrings.

YVONNE SPAENE/CATERS NEWS

Is this the most photogenic insect?

Like puppets from a children's TV show, these bizarre-looking creatures seem to be posing for the camera. Though often referred to as false stick insects, they are actually horsehead grasshoppers.

Their appearance as bulbous-eyed twigs is an adaptation to help them blend in with trees in the Peruvian rainforest. "Some grasshoppers in other parts of the world have an elongated shape and a slanted face, but not as extreme as this," says Dr George McGavin, entomologist and BBC presenter. "The females reach about 16cm in length and they can jump a fair way."

In fact, neurobiologists from the University of Leicester have discovered that horsehead grasshoppers jump without using muscles thanks to the unusual properties in their limbs and joints. It is hoped this could help in the development of robotic and prosthetic limbs.

For more great pictures, follow us on http://pinterest.com/sciencefocus

PLANET EARTH

There is much about our planet's make-up that is still unknown to scientists. However, there are plenty of mysteries that have been solved – here are some of the most intriguing...

HOW ARE RISING SEA LEVELS MEASURED?

It's a combination of measurements collected from tide gauges and satellite altimetry. Tide gauge data needs to be averaged over long periods to even out differences in sea level caused by tides and atmospheric pressure. Satellites can measure altitude to a precision of 20mm, but they need to be constantly recalibrated to allow for orbital decay. Each system is used to refine the measurements of the other.

HOW DOES GRANITE FORM?

Granite is made of magma that solidifies more readily than the magma around it. This occurs because, in most mixtures of molten minerals, there's a specific proportion that has a higher melting point than the others. This is called a eutectic mixture.

In the same way that fractional distillation changes the ratio of different mixed liquids, fractional crystallisation separates the lower melting point compounds and drives the magma towards its eutectic composition.

When the magma cools below its specific melting point, it solidifies into a huge lump, called a pluton. This works its way up to the surface through geological weak points and can be exposed on the surface when the softer, sedimentary rock above it wears away.

ALAMY X3

WHY DOES THE MOON AFFECT EARTH'S TIDES MORE THAN THE SUN DOES?

The tides are the result of the difference between the forces of gravity on opposite sides of Earth. Because Earth's diameter is such a small fraction of the Sun-Earth distance, the Sun's gravitational pull changes by only 0.017 per cent across Earth. But for the Moon, that difference is 6.8 per cent, 400 times greater. If you factor in the overall stronger pull from the Sun, this means the Sun's tidal effect is only about 44 per cent that of the Moon.

HOW MANY TREES ARE NEEDED FOR ENOUGH OXYGEN FOR ONE PERSON?

Trees release oxygen when they use energy from sunlight to make glucose from carbon dioxide and water. Like all plants, trees also use oxygen when they split glucose back down to release energy to power their metabolisms. Averaged over a 24-hour period, they produce more oxygen than they use up; otherwise there would be no net gain in growth.

It takes six molecules of CO_2 to produce one molecule of glucose by photosynthesis, and six molecules of oxygen are released as a by-product. A glucose molecule contains six carbon atoms, so that's a net gain of one molecule of oxygen for every atom of carbon added to the tree. A mature sycamore tree might be around 12m tall and weigh two tonnes, including the roots and leaves. If it grows by five per cent each year, it will produce around 100kg of wood, of which 38kg will be carbon. Allowing for the relative molecular weights of oxygen and carbon, this equates to 100kg of oxygen per tree per year.

A human breathes about 9.5 tonnes of air in a year, but oxygen only makes up about 23 percent of that air, by mass, and we only extract a little over a third of the oxygen from each breath. That works out to a total of about 740kg of oxygen per year - which is, very roughly, seven or eight trees' worth.

IS THE MELTING OF ANTARCTICA'S ICE BOOSTING SEA LEVELS?

As the biggest expanse of continental ice on the planet, Antarctica would seem the most likely source of increasing sea levels as its ice melts through global warming. In reality, however, current measurements suggest that the amount of ice lost from Antarctica through melting is being roughly matched by the formation of fresh ice. As a result, Antarctica is thought to contribute only around 10 per cent of the sea-level rise attributable to melting ice.

ALAMY X2, THINKSTOCK, NASA/CORBIS

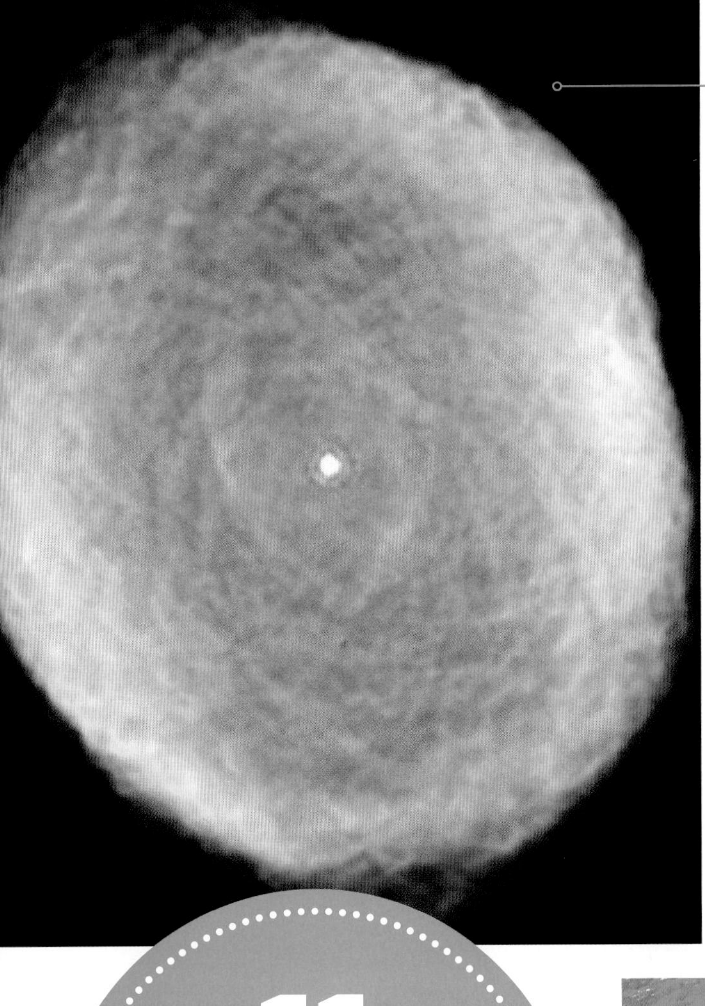

IF A HOLE WERE DRILLED THROUGH EARTH, WHAT WOULD HAPPEN TO A BALL DROPPED INTO IT?

The usual answer to this 'thought experiment' says the ball would accelerate under gravity, reaching a speed of over 28,000km/h at Earth's centre before rising back up to the surface on the opposite side of Earth, arriving some 42 minutes after release. It would then fall back again and repeat the journey endlessly. But this ignores the Earth's rotation. In 2004, mathematician Dr Andrew Simoson of King College, Tennessee, published an analysis of the problem, showing that as the ball falls through Earth, the force of gravity gets weaker towards the centre. Given that the speed of rotation of Earth decreases with depth, the tunnel through which the ball travels would need to be curved to ensure the ball falls without hitting the sides.

Dr Simoson believes his calculations may explain the bizarre appearance of the Spirograph Nebula (pictured), found by the Hubble Space Telescope in 1999. Debris in this cosmic cloud feels gravity in the same way as the dropped ball, which may explain its strange curved lines.

11

billion is the UN's latest estimate of the size of the world's population will be by 2100. This is an increase on the previous estimate of 10.1 billion.

WHY DON'T WE GET BIG EARTHQUAKES IN THE UK?

Big earthquakes are caused by tectonic plates sliding past each other in a juddering motion. This builds a massive amount of pressure before it's released suddenly and unpredictably. Britain is on the Eurasian plate, about 1,600km (1,000 miles) from the nearest boundary to the west. And it's moving away from the neighbouring plate, so there's no energy build-up.

HOW MUCH SALT IS IN THE DEAD SEA?

The Dead Sea has a salinity of 33.7 per cent. This is almost 10 times saltier than ordinary seawater. If you evaporated a litre of Dead Sea water, you'd have around 250g of salt left behind, and in the whole of the Dead Sea there are about 37 billion tonnes of the stuff.

Ordinary sea salt is 97 per cent sodium chloride, whereas Dead Sea salt is a mixture of lots of different chloride and bromide salts. Ordinary sodium chloride only makes up about 30 per cent. That's still enough to supply the entire population of the UK with cooking salt for 70,000 years!

CAN EARTH BE ARTIFICIALLY COOLED?

One obvious way to offset the effects of global warming is to boost Earth's albedo – its ability to reflect the Sun's heat back into space. Clouds, dust and other 'aerosols' like particles from volcanic eruptions do this naturally. US-based aerospace company Aurora Flight Sciences claim that using balloons to release millions of tonnes of sulphur dioxide into the stratosphere each year could cool the Earth by 1 to 2°C. One drawback is the cost, estimated at around $10 billion a year. However, there are potentially unintended consequences of trying to tweak the complex set of interactions that make up the Earth's climate.

THINKSTOCK X7, NASA, SCIENCE PHOTO LIBRARY/CHRISTIAN DARKIN

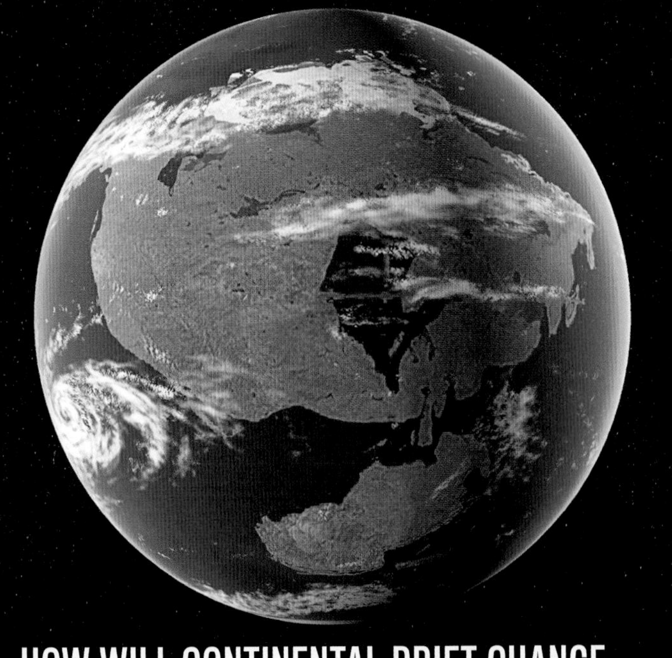

HOW WILL CONTINENTAL DRIFT CHANGE EARTH IN THE FUTURE?

The world's continents may seem like 'terra firma', but in reality they're giant rafts of relatively light rock floating around Earth's surface. Precision measurements using satellites have revealed that Europe and North America are moving apart at around 30mm a year, while the Pacific is expanding four times faster still, making upheaval and changes in the appearance of our planet inevitable.

Geologists believe the result of this slo-mo action will be the formation of one gigantic supercontinent over the next 250 million years. Such supercontinents are thought to have existed many times during Earth's history, but their appearance depends on many factors, such as the speed and direction of the resulting collisions.

Using current measurements, Professor Chris Scotese of the University of Texas, Arlington, has carried out computer simulations that suggest Africa, Europe and the Americas will come together around the equator, trapping a huge expanse of sea between them.

WHY ARE THE TALLEST TREES ON EARTH NOT EVEN TALLER?

The reason trees have a trunk at all is to raise the leaves above other vegetation to maximise the amount of light they receive. Once a sapling is taller than the shrubs and ground vegetation, it will continue to grow because it is competing with other, older trees in its vicinity.

However, the bigger the tree, the more likely it is to blow down or be struck by lightning, which tends to weed out the bigger specimens. To grow taller, a tree also needs to grow thicker, so growth slows down over time. The tallest trees are more than 2,500 years old, which is a long time to keep dodging disease and disaster.

TOP TEN

HIGHEST MOUNTAINS

1. Everest
Height: 8,848m
Location: Nepal/China

2. K2
Height: 8,611m
Location: Pakistan/China

3. Kangchenjunga
Height: 8,586m
Location: Nepal/India

4. Lhotse
Height: 8,516m
Location: Nepal/China

5. Makalu
Height: 8,418m
Location: Nepal/China

6. Cho Oyu
Height: 8,201mm
Location: Nepal/China

7. Dhaulagiri
Height: 8,167m
Location: Nepal

8. Manaslu
Height: 8,156m
Location: Nepal

9. Nanga Parbat
Height: 8,126m
Location: Pakistan

10. Annapurna
Height: 8,126m
Location: Nepal

ARE SOME PLANTS BETTER THAN OTHERS AT SUCKING UP CARBON DIOXIDE?

Plants use carbon dioxide (CO_2) during photosynthesis to make glucose. It takes six molecules of CO_2 to make every molecule of glucose, and this basic building block is then used for energy and to make the structure of the plant itself. This biochemical reaction is the same for all plants, but the faster a plant grows, the more carbon dioxide it will use up per second. By that measure, bamboo might be the best at sucking up CO_2. However, fast-growing plants tend not to live long and when a plant dies, all the carbon in the plant is broken down by insects, fungi and microbes, and released as CO_2 again.

So the plants that are considered the most adept at locking away carbon dioxide from the atmosphere are the longest-living ones with the most mass - hardwood trees. It's all temporary, though. Eventually every plant returns all the carbon dioxide it uses back to the atmosphere.

AT WHAT DISTANCE DOES EARTH NO LONGER PULL ON AN OBJECT?

Strictly speaking, Earth's gravity will always pull on an object, no matter how distant. Gravity is a force that obeys an 'inverse square law'. So, for example, put an object twice as far away and it will feel a quarter of the force. Put it four times further away and it will feel one-sixteenth the force. But however far away the object is, it will always feel the pull of gravity, even though it might be vanishingly small.

DID YOU KNOW?

The largest reef system in the northern hemisphere is the Belize Barrier Reef, a 963km^2 submarine shelf and barrier reef stretching from Mexico to Guatemala. Only Australia's Great Barrier Reef is bigger.

IS EVERY SNOWFLAKE REALLY UNIQUE IN SHAPE?

There's very little chance of any two of the classic six-sided, spiky snowflakes exactly matching each other in every detail. But that's not the only type of snowflake: some are far less complex - and two looking remarkably similar were found by American scientists on a collection plate aboard an aircraft in November 1986.

ALAMY X3, THINKSTOCK X2

IS IT POSSIBLE TO HARNESS THE POWER OF FALLING RAIN?

A 2008 French study estimated that you could use piezoelectric devices, which generate power when they move, to extract 12 milliwatts from a raindrop. Over a year, this would amount to less than 0.001kWh per square metre - enough to power a remote sensor. A better idea would be to collect the water and use it to drive a turbine. The UK receives just under a tonne of water per square metre per year. For a house with a 185m^2 roof, this would amount to 3kWh of energy per year. With a 60 per cent conversion efficiency, it's enough to run a 15W light bulb for 133 hours. That's still a lot less than solar energy; we receive 60,000 times more energy per square metre from the Sun than from rain.

HOW DO PLANTS GROW TOWARDS THE LIGHT?

Plant cells contain a protein called phototropin that is mostly concentrated in the growing tip of the plant shoot. This protein unfolds into an activated state when it absorbs blue wavelengths of light. This sets off a cascade of interactions between different proteins in the cells, which ultimately changes the alignment of cellular scaffolding proteins, called microtubules. The upshot of this is that the cells on the darker side of the shoot elongate, while those on the light side remain squat and boxy. As the dark side of the plant grows longer, the shoot as a whole bends away from that side and towards the light.

Recent research at the Carnegie Institution at Stanford University, and Wageningen University in the Netherlands, found that the rearrangement of the microtubules can happen surprisingly quickly. Within minutes of exposure to blue light, plant cells will start making new microtubules.

WHAT WOULD HAPPEN IF ALL THE CORAL REEFS DISAPPEARED?

Our planet would be a different place. In the 1950s, when research began, many coral reefs were thriving, but since then about 20 per cent have been lost through increasing sea temperatures and acidification.

Reefs are built by tiny organisms called corals and are home to about a quarter of all marine species, even though they cover only 0.1 per cent of the oceans. If they all disappeared tomorrow, an entire ecosystem would be lost, drastically reducing our planet's biodiversity. For humans, coral reefs provide abundant fishing resources, as well as protection for some low-lying islands and lucrative tourist destinations. About 850 million people live within 100km of a reef, of whom about a third depend on it for their food or livelihood.

If the sea temperature and acidity were favourable the day after tomorrow, then the reefs would quickly begin to grow back, but if climate change continues, they might never do so.

ALAMY X2, AFP/GETTY IMAGES, NASA/JPL-CALTECH/UMD

WHY DOESN'T LIGHTNING TRAVEL IN A STRAIGHT LINE?

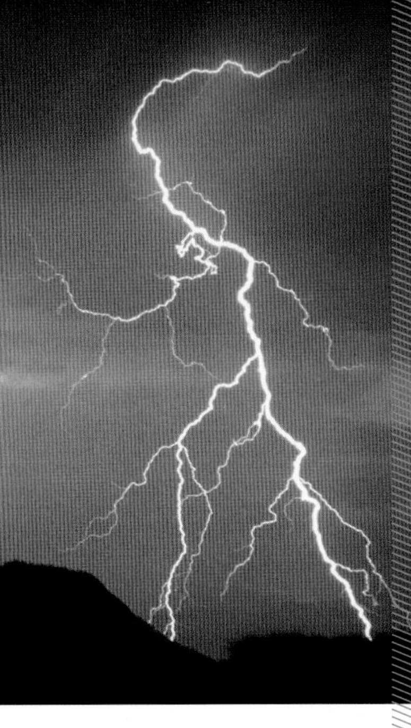

The zig-zagging path of lightning has its origin in processes still not fully understood. It begins with strong rising currents of air creating a static electric charge through frictional effects somewhat like those on the surface of balloons rubbed on suitable fabric. This charge generates an electric field that accelerates any free electrons in the surrounding air, smashing them into neighbouring molecules, thus releasing yet more electrons.

If sufficiently violent, these collisions will turn the air under the cloud from electrically insulating to conducting, which allows the passage of electrical current. This heats the air to around 30,000°C, triggering the characteristic flash of light that follows the zig-zag path formed by the collisions. That heat also causes a sudden expansion of the air, which we hear as a clap of thunder.

WHAT'S THE WORLD'S LARGEST BUILDING?

As measured by total floor area, the largest freestanding building is the New Century Global Centre in Chengdu, China. It's big enough to hold 16 Wembley Stadiums or 20 Sydney Opera Houses. At 1.7 million square metres, the floor area is almost four times the size of Vatican City. It's a huge shopping mall, but it also has a convention centre, hotel, ice skating rink, IMAX cinema, mock Mediterranean village and a swimming pool with an LED screen 150m wide that displays tropical sunsets to visitors lazing on an artificial beach.

WHERE DID EARTH'S WATER COME FROM?

It's a bit of a mystery. Explanations divide into two camps: endogenous, meaning the water came from the Earth itself, and exogenous, meaning it was dumped here from elsewhere.

For example, one endogenous possibility is that water molecules were formed from hydrogen and oxygen molecules combining inside the early Earth, and emerging as steam in volcanic eruptions. Alternatively, ready-made water molecules may have been delivered here by comets.

Until recently, astronomers were sceptical of the comet theory, as it could not explain the fact that around 0.3 per cent of oceanic water contains an unusual form of hydrogen called deuterium. However, in 2011, astronomers found deuterium-based water on comet Hartley 2. While not proof that we've all been drinking comet debris, it keeps this intriguing possibility alive.

ABB

What are these silver spheres?

These huge orbs form part of a facility in Ludvika in Sweden developing the next generation of power transmission technology. Leading engineering company ABB's High Voltage Laboratory puts new pieces of equipment, such as circuit breakers and transformers, through their paces to test whether they can cope with high-voltage transmission.

Made of aluminium, the spheres sit on top of the test circuit. "They even out the electrical field preventing flashovers – short circuits through the air between different pieces of equipment," says engineering manager Björn Jacobson. The spheres are part of an alternating current (AC) test circuit where equipment can be exposed to over one million volts.

For more great pictures, follow us on http://pinterest.com/sciencefocus

HUMAN BRAIN

Despite making up just 2 per cent of total body weight, up to 25 per cent of the body's energy is spent on fuelling this powerful organ that controls everything - from what we do to how we act

WHY ARE REPETITIVE NOISES SO ANNOYING?

They keep on attracting our attention and prevent us from concentrating on other things. We quickly habituate (stop reacting) to some repetitive sounds, especially regular ones such as ticking clocks, but not to others. Speed matters, with slowly dripping taps being especially maddening. The main reason is lack of control - if you know you can stop the noise at any time, you will not find it annoying.

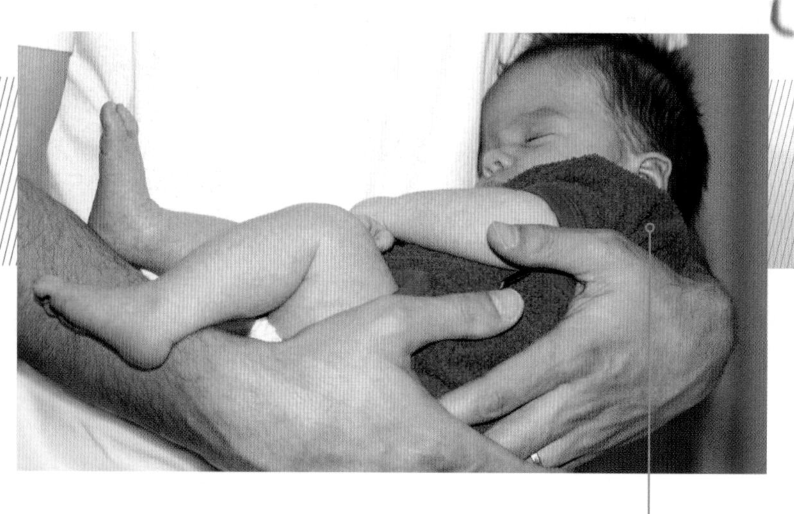

CAN YOU HYPNOTISE A BABY TO SLEEP?

There is still no clear scientific consensus on whether hypnosis constitutes a separate state of consciousness, or merely a sort of socially conditioned, imaginative role-play. MRI scans and EEG measurements have failed to find anything that corresponds to a hypnotic trance, for example. The non-state interpretation of hypnosis assumes that the person being hypnotised understands both what is being said to them and what is expected of them as subjects of hypnosis. That seems doubtful in the case of babies.

What's more, the techniques that might be used to 'hypnotise' babies - focusing your attention fully on them; speaking in a low, steady voice; gently rocking, and so on - are much the same as the ones you would use to just send a baby to sleep naturally. And if your baby falls asleep, then by definition it isn't hypnotised.

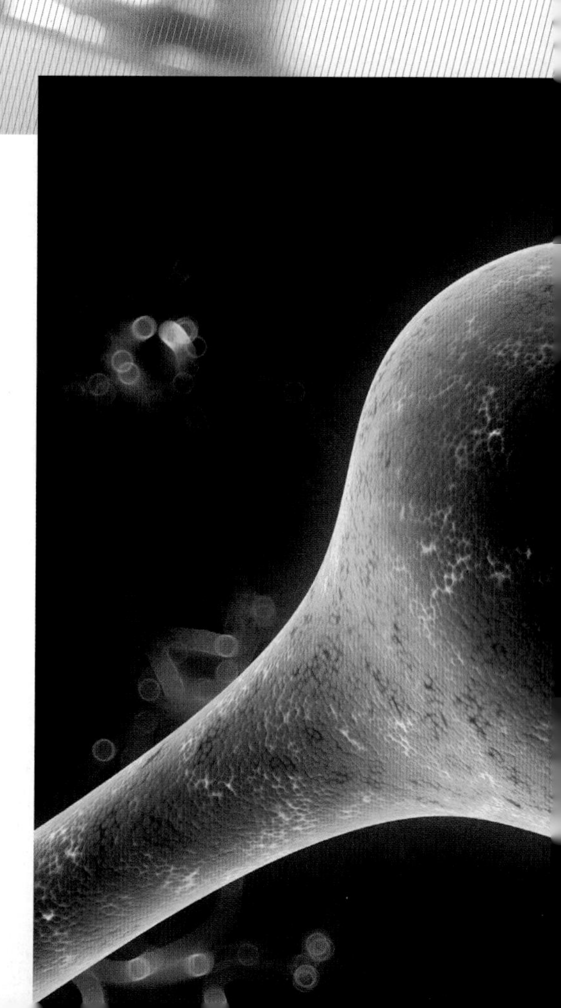

CAN YOU DREAM IN A LANGUAGE YOU DON'T SPEAK?

Most dreams don't involve clear speech of any kind. Any 'speech' is just a jumble of concepts, intuitions and ideas that are understood by the characters in your dream without being fully articulated. It's quite possible to believe you are speaking a foreign language in your dream, but there is no reason to assume that it's any more real than the dream sensation that you can fly.

HOW IS A MEMORY FORMED?

There is really no such thing as 'a memory'. Memory is a process, or a set of inter-related processes, in which the brain changes in response to events. These changes result in us being able to repeat a name or number (short-term memory), recall a specific event (episodic memory), recite a poem we learned at school (long-term memory) or exercise a learned skill, such as riding a bike or skateboarding (procedural memory).

Among the important mechanisms that underlie memory are changes to the strength of synapses (the gaps between nerve cells that signals have to cross), the growth of the tiny dendritic spines that grow out of the cells' branching dendrites, and many chemical changes that strengthen some networks of neurones at the expense of others. These changes occur all over the brain but some areas, such as the tiny hippocampus in the temporal lobe of the brain, are especially important. Damage here can mean a permanent loss of any ability to lay down new memories.

TOP TEN
MOST SPOKEN LANGUAGES

Source: www.ethonologue.com. Figures are estimates of first-tongue speakers

1. Mandarin Chinese
Speakers worldwide: 848m

2. Spanish
Speakers worldwide: 406m

3. English
Speakers worldwide: 335m

4. Hindi
Speakers worldwide: 260m

5. Arabic
Speakers worldwide: 223m

6. Portuguese
Speakers worldwide: 202m

7. Bengali
Speakers worldwide: 193m

8. Russian
Speakers worldwide: 162m

9. Japanese
Speakers worldwide: 122m

10. Javanese (Indonesia)
Speakers worldwide: 84.3m

WHAT HAPPENS WHEN SOMETHING IS ON THE TIP OF YOUR TONGUE?

There are two main theories for something being on the 'tip of your tongue'. One claims that the memory for the word is there but just not strong enough to be accessed. The other suggests that the person's memory provides genuine clues about the target word but cannot piece them together well enough. Emotional questions increase the chance of it happening and sometimes the answer just springs to mind some time later.

DID YOU KNOW?

The first sense to develop while in the womb is the sense of touch. The lips and cheeks can experience touch at about eight weeks and the rest of the body around 12 weeks.

HOW DO WE LEARN TO WALK?

Much of our ability to walk upright appears to be hard-wired: simply holding infants upright and moving them across the floor is enough to make them take 'baby steps'.

New research shows that we inherited some of the necessary brain circuitry from other mammals, such as rats. What makes us different is that by the time we become toddlers, we're using this circuitry in much more sophisticated ways, allowing us to both walk upright and grasp things at the same time.

IF A PERSON IS BORN BLIND AND DEAF, WHAT LANGUAGE DO THEY THINK IN?

Not all thinking requires language. We can think in pictures, 3D patterns, bodily gestures, movements, and almost anything else we have experienced. Deaf signers use language to think with, but experience it through imagined movements of their hands rather than as sounds. If a deaf and blind child is never taught language, they have to rely on other ways of thinking. Most, however, are taught language through some kind of signing. In the most famous case, Helen Keller (right) became deaf and blind at 19 months. Her teacher spelled words on her hands and she went on to become a writer and political campaigner. Presumably she thought using this language of touch.

DO YOU BURN MORE CALORIES DURING DEEP THOUGHT?

Yes, but the difference is tiny. The common claim that the brain uses 20 per cent of the body's energy for only two per cent of body weight makes it sound very demanding. But this only applies if you keep still. Physical exercise quickly demands lots more calories to power the muscles, while deep thought needs only a few, even if it makes you hungry. In one study, some students did intense computer work while others relaxed. There was almost no difference in energy used, but those doing mental work ate about 200 more calories afterwards.

This may be because the brain uses glucose for fuel and intense thought lowers blood glucose levels. Another reason is that the brain never stops controlling breathing, digestion and other bodily functions. At night it is busy dreaming and by day processing information from the senses. All this takes less than one calorie a minute. So even if deep thought doubled the calories used, this would be a small increase compared with getting up and doing something physical.

WHY DO WE GET TIRED?

Tiredness is a warning signal to encourage us to rest. Sleepiness is governed by the levels of the hormones adenosine and melatonin, which gradually accumulate during the day. The function of sleep isn't well understood, but it seems to be important for tissue repair and growth, as well as memory processing. It isn't simply a question of conserving energy. Hibernating squirrels will periodically raise their body temperature to enable them to transition from hibernation to ordinary sleep. This shows that sleep is an active process that is worth spending energy on, even in a completely resting animal.

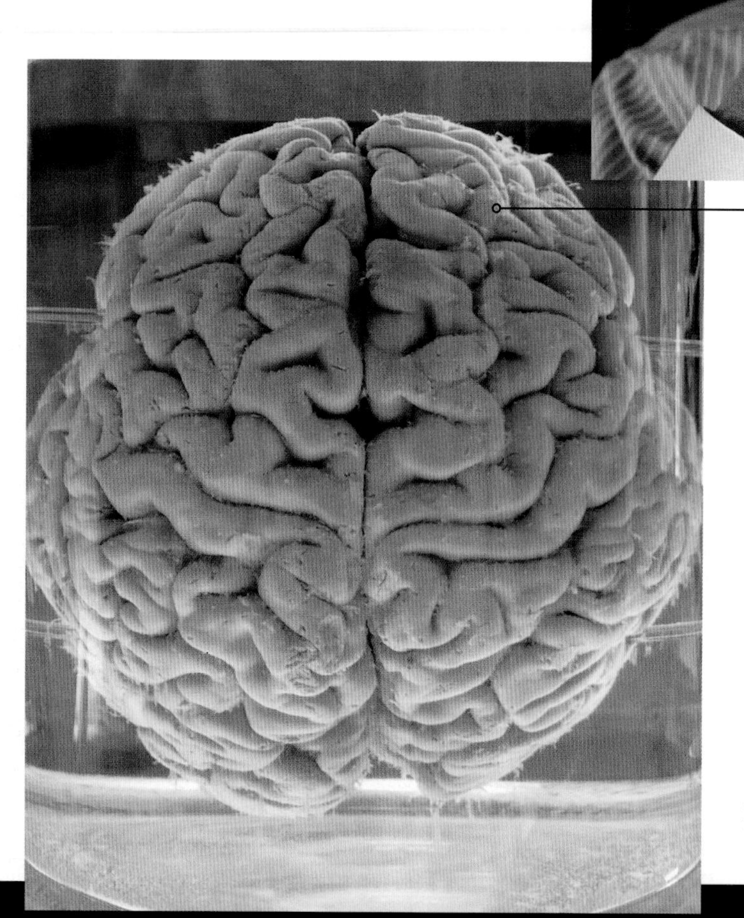

COULD A BRAIN BE KEPT ALIVE INDEPENDENTLY OF A BODY?

Gruesomely, the answer is yes - at least for a while. As long ago as 1925, Dr Sergei Briukhonenko of the Chemical-Pharmaceutical Institute in Moscow showed that the severed heads of animals could be kept alive for several hours if connected up to a crude version of what became the life-saving heart-lung machine.

WHY DO WE GASP WHEN WE ARE SCARED?

Probably to grab a little extra oxygen. Gasping is part of the fight-or-flight response in which adrenalin and other hormones are released to prepare the body for action. These dilate pupils, speed up heart rate, breathing and metabolic rate, and supply more fuel to the muscles. All these changes mean using oxygen more quickly, so a good deep gasp might be a useful precaution.

THINKSTOCK X4

WHY DOES IT FEEL STRANGE TO WALK UP A NON-WORKING ESCALATOR?

This is called the 'broken escalator phenomenon'. Each time we walk or ride on a moving escalator, our brains are learning to expect that escalators move. We then progressively fine-tune the motor control of our legs and the balance mechanisms of the inner ear to account for the motion. Even when we know that an escalator isn't moving, our conscious awareness of this isn't enough to override the unconscious brain that recognises the grooved metal staircase as an escalator and therefore expects it to move.

Scientists at Imperial College London investigated the phenomenon in 2004 and found that walking on a moving platform just 20 times was enough to condition the brain to expect it to still be moving on the 21st attempt, even though subjects were told in advance that it would not be.

DOES A BRAINWAVE EQUATE TO A MENTAL STATE?

No. The term 'brainwave' comes from the patterns detected by an apparatus called the electroencephalogram (EEG) that measures electrical signals from electrodes on the scalp. The overall frequency gives an indication of a person's mental state. For example, 'alpha waves' (8-13 per second) are associated with a relaxed state. But these surface waves are created from millions of small electrical signals in the underlying brain, so they are a very crude measure that could not equate to a precise mental state.

If you mean to ask whether any kind of brain process equates to a mental state, then you are in the realms of seriously difficult philosophical questions. 'Identity theorists' say yes – mental states really are brain states. 'Functionalists' argue that the function being carried out equates to mental states. For instance, if a human brain and a computer were both trying to solve the same chess problem, they would be in the same mental state.

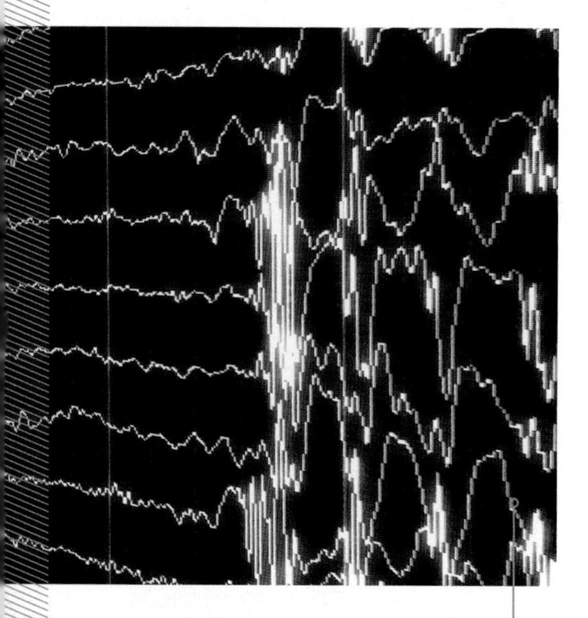

IS IT BETTER TO GET TO SLEEP EARLIER?

Yes, your brain moves through different sleep states during the night. Rapid eye movement (REM) sleep is the shallowest, and then there are three progressively deeper non-REM sleep stages. You will normally cycle from REM to deeper sleep four or five times in a night, but the deepest sleep stage lasts much longer in the early part of the night. This is controlled by your personal daily cycle of the hormone melatonin, not the time that you go to bed. After about 3am, the brain skips the deepest sleep stage altogether. And lying in late only gives you more REM sleep, which is less restful.

IS EINSTEIN THE SMARTEST PERSON WHO HAS EVER LIVED?

Einstein has become synonymous with brilliance and he's certainly one of the greatest scientists of all time. But it's hard to claim he's the smartest person who ever lived. It's often said (with scant evidence) that his IQ was 160; even if true, that would make him less intelligent than thousands of people alive today. In terms of mathematical ability, Einstein would not come close to matching today's leading physicists like Stephen Hawking (right).

The depth and range of his achievements are not without precedent, either. Far less well-known scientists such as Carl Gauss and Leonhard Euler made fundamental contributions in many more fields. The person with perhaps the strongest claim to being the smartest person of all time is the Victorian polymath Sir Francis Galton, whose work on everything from statistics and evolution to the 'wisdom of crowds' is still used every day by researchers a century after his death.

THINKSTOCK, ALAMY X4

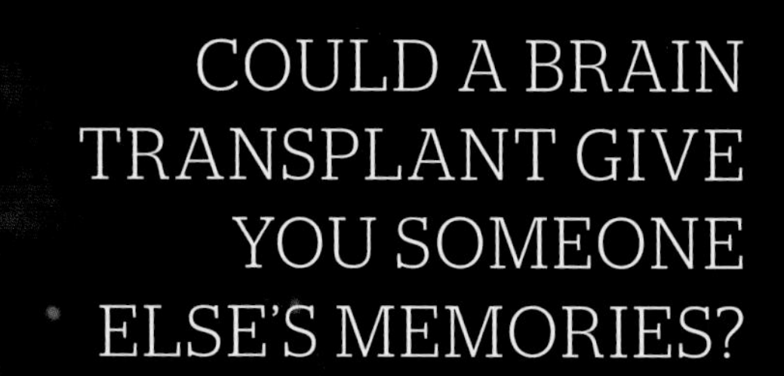

COULD A BRAIN TRANSPLANT GIVE YOU SOMEONE ELSE'S MEMORIES?

There's no such thing as a brain transplant. Not just because we don't currently have the technique, but because putting someone else's brain in your body would result in them getting a body transplant, not you getting a brain transplant! Your body would have their memories, but it would also have their personality - 'you' wouldn't get their memories because 'you' wouldn't exist any more. Transplanting just part of their brain wouldn't work either, because memory is distributed among lots of different regions of the brain. Virtually every part has some role to play in storing or processing memories.

$100m is being invested in the BRAIN projects by the US government to map the human brain in an attempt to better understand and treat diseases like Parkinson's and Alzheimer's.

IS THE BRAIN OF A GENIUS HEAVIER THAN AN AVERAGE BRAIN?

Possibly, yes, but size alone cannot explain why some of us are regarded as geniuses. Some large-brained animals such as dolphins and whales are very intelligent, but so are crows with their tiny brains.

The brains of geniuses such as Albert Einstein have been measured, but no relationship with size or weight was found. One study revealed that Einstein had more glial cells than average. These support and protect neurones, suggesting that his brain demanded more energy.

Other studies show that geniuses have more long-range neural connections that reach from one area of the brain to another. Yet no single feature explains their exceptional abilities. Persistence, hard work and determination may be just as important, and they do not require an especially heavy brain.

What happens to the blood you donate?

In a room maintained at exactly 22°C hang hundreds of bags of donated blood. Each year, NHS Blood and Transplant's Filton Blood Centre in Bristol handles enough of the red stuff to completely replace the blood of over 85,000 people – that's roughly the population of Halifax or Hastings. It's the world's largest blood bank.

Blood from all over southwest England is delivered overnight. "It is kept at 22°C during shipment, and remains at 22°C while it's being treated – that's the optimum temperature to avoid it clotting," says the centre's manager, John Kirkwood.

First, the white blood cells are removed in circular filters. Part of the body's defence system, these are given to patients with life-threatening infections, to boost their immune systems. The remaining filtered blood is then separated into red cells and plasma. The former is given to patients who have suffered heavy blood loss, while the latter can help those who have been severely shocked or burned.

For more great pictures, follow us on http://pinterest.com/sciencefocus

DAVID HEDGES/SWNS.COM

TRANSPORT

The past century completely transformed the way we travel. But we're still obsessed with making our modes of transport bigger and faster

WHY DO YOU GET MORE JET LAGGED WHEN TRAVELLING WEST-EAST?

It's partly because flying west extends the length of the day, so if you take off in daylight, you will probably be in daylight for the entire flight, which makes sleeping on the plane difficult. But it also has to do with our circadian rhythms. There is some evidence that we can adjust our body clocks by 90 minutes a day when setting the clocks back (travelling from east to west), but only by an hour a day when setting them forwards (west to east). Flights from Los Angeles to Heathrow, for example, often also take off in the late afternoon, which makes it mid-morning local time when you land - so you have to wait longer until a socially acceptable bedtime.

WHAT IS THE FUEL CONSUMPTION OF AN OCEAN LINER?

An ocean liner burns about 120 litres of fuel per kilometre, compared to your car that gets through, say, 0.06 litres per kilometre. A jumbo jet consumes 12 litres per kilometer. But with 500 passengers, the jet can fly each person 42km on a litre of fuel. The ship manages 25km per litre per passenger, assuming 3,000 people on board. A car carries four passengers, so it's 67km per litre per passenger.

WHICH POLICE CAR IS THE FASTEST IN THE WORLD?

Don't try outrunning the police in Italy, especially if the officers are in the force's most prized motors, a couple of Lamborghini Gallardo LP560-4s (pictured). They have 5.2-litre V10 engines, accelerating from 0 to 96km/h in 2.5 seconds. The car's top speed is 320km/h.

However, nearly as impressive is the UK's fastest police bike. The US police use it, too. It is the fearsome Suzuki Hayabusa: with its 1300cc engine, it is one of the world's fastest production bikes, capable of 312km/h. It would almost give the Lamborghini a run for its money.

IS RAIL TRANSPORT OF GOODS MORE EFFICIENT THAN ROADS?

Purely on a fuel-per-tonne-per-mile basis, rail transport is more efficient in almost every case. Trains travel on narrow rails with hard wheels. This reduces the contact area and almost eliminates flexing of the wheels, so the rolling resistance is about one-seventh that of rubber tyres on tarmac. Coupling wagons together allows a train to pull a very heavy load without increasing its cross-sectional area, so wind resistance is kept low. In contrast, if you try to couple more than two lorry wagons together, they become prone to fish-tailing.

Perhaps most importantly, trains travel on smooth tracks, without sharp bends, steep inclines or start-stop motion through heavy traffic. As a result, studies in the US have shown rail transport to be up to five times more fuel-efficient for comparable journeys. However, rail infrastructure is much more capital-intensive than a road network, and the efficiency gains are much lower for light consumer goods than for bulk commodities like coal and iron ore.

DO SINKING SHIPS REALLY SUCK NEARBY OBJECTS DOWN WITH THEM?

In the early 20th century, this was widely held to be the case and the advice was for lifeboats launched from a sinking ship to row hard away to avoid being pulled down with it. This may have contributed to the loss of life on the Titanic, as only 13 survivors were pulled from the water. Some survivors report struggling against a powerful suction, while others claim to have been able to step off the sinking ship without their head even going under.

There are two proposed mechanisms for the suction effect. The first is the slipstream. As the boat slides under the surface, it creates a current of water that flows down with it due to friction with the side of the hull and vortices are created as the water closes up behind the boat. The second idea is that air trapped inside the ship is released as it sinks, in a stream of bubbles that lower the effective density of the surrounding water and reduce your buoyancy to the point where you sink. The bubble theory isn't well supported by evidence; in fact, the rising bubbles generate a slipstream of their own that can actually push you upwards.

Whatever the cause, the effect seems to have been exaggerated. There are no reports of lifeboats being dragged under by a sinking ship, but in the case of a very large ship like the Titanic, the slipstream may have been enough to drag people down for a few metres.

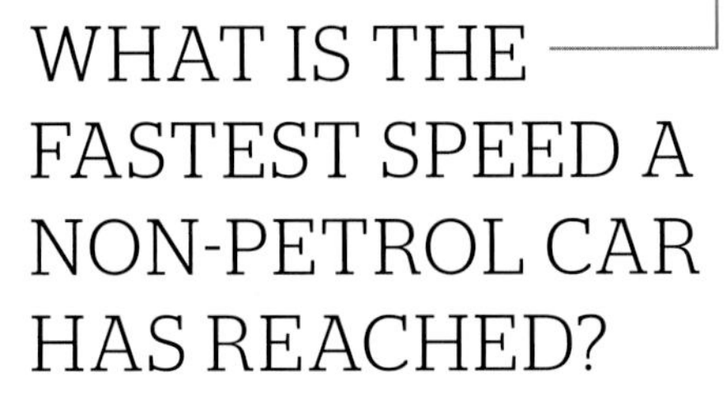

WHAT IS THE FASTEST SPEED A NON-PETROL CAR HAS REACHED?

When it comes to biofuels, engineering students from Boise State University in Idaho hold the record for the fastest vegetable-oil-powered car. In November 2011, they achieved 248.5km/h (155.3mph) in a Chevrolet S-10 pickup running on cottonseed and sunflower oil. The 5.9 litre-engine truck was fitted with a mechanical injection system, a separate tank for vegetable oil and a heating assembly to reduce the oil's viscosity, helping it run through the fuel system.

But, of course, the fastest non-petrol car is the Thrust SSC, the current land speed record-holder, which achieved 1,228km/h in October 1997. It had turbofan engines powered by kerosene aviation fuel.

WHY AREN'T AIRSHIPS USED ANYMORE?

Early airships competed against steamships. They carried smaller loads, but were faster and could travel directly to inland cities. Aeroplanes, however, are much faster and can carry more, which offsets their higher fuel costs. Airships are also trickier to handle at take-off and landing. A few are still used for tourist flights and surveying.

THINKSTOCK, HOLLY SALEWSKI, SCIENCE PHOTO LIBRARY

HOW FAST CAN A HUMAN SAFELY TRAVEL?

It's not speed that's dangerous; it's the sudden stop. In fact, we can't directly perceive speed at all, only acceleration and the relative speed between us and another object. We're travelling at 720,000km/h right now, as our Solar System orbits the centre of the Galaxy.

What is a safe speed depends on the obstacles in your way and the thickness of the medium you're travelling through. Provided you had a spaceship with enough fuel and you could plot a course that avoided any solid objects, it would be quite possible to get within 0.1 per cent of the speed of light.

3.64

million people pass through Tokyo's Shinjuku station each day. According to the *Guinness Book of Records*, it is the busiest train station in the world.

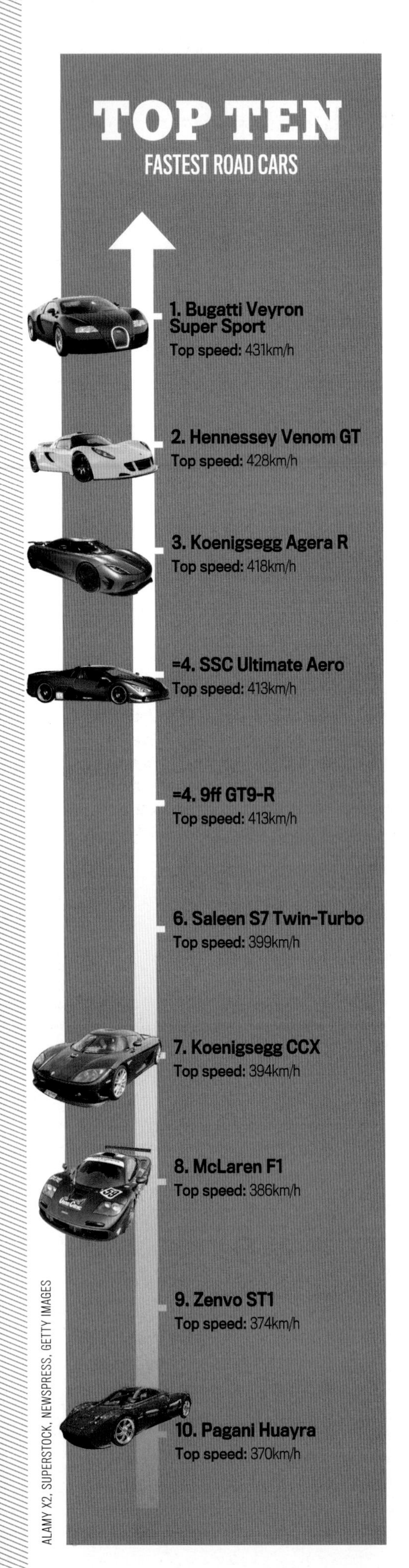

CAN YOU SAVE FUEL BY SLIPSTREAMING OTHER VEHICLES?

Yes. Vehicles create a region of relatively low-pressure air behind them and it is indeed possible to reduce fuel consumption by getting into this slipstream. According to research published last year by the University of Aachen, Germany, lorries can save around 17 per cent in fuel by tailgating each other. Don't try it yourself, though.

HOW DO PLANES FLY UPSIDE DOWN?

Almost 110 years after the Wright Brothers first flew a powered aircraft, physicists still struggle to come up with a simple explanation for the way that planes generate lift. And it's more complicated when a plane is upside down.

One way to think of lift is to imagine the wing deflecting the stream of air that passes over it, like the jet from a rocket. Airflow tends to adhere to the surface of the wing, and the shape of the wing (the airfoil) deflects the air running over it in a curve that ends up pointing downwards at the trailing edge. By forcing the air to move downwards, you create an upward force on the plane.

When the wing is horizontal, this airfoil deflection is the only source of lift for the plane. But if the wing is tilted upwards, the air that strikes the underside of the wing is also deflected downwards. The steeper the angle, the more the deflected air on the underside contributes to the total lift. When you fly a plane upside down, you just need to make sure that the inverted wings are angled enough that the lift from the underside is sufficient to compensate for the fact that the airfoil is upside down and generates some lift.

ALAMY X2, SUPERSTOCK, NEWSPRESS, GETTY IMAGES

WHAT'S THE LOWEST A PLANE CAN REFUEL IN MID-AIR?

Refuelling at altitudes as low as 300m (1,000ft) has been examined as a strategy to keep strike planes below the enemy radar horizon. But it's much more dangerous if the refuelling plane needs to disengage suddenly. Tanker planes aren't very manoeuvrable, so this task is almost always performed above 6,000m (20,000ft).

HOW MUCH ENERGY DOES IT TAKE TO MANUFACTURE AN AVERAGE CAR?

This is a tricky thing to calculate. You can't just measure the electricity and gas bills of a car manufacturing plant and divide it by the number of cars made in that time. That wouldn't include the cost of mining and refining the materials used at the plant. But a detailed study by the US Department of Energy in 2010 came up with an average value of 34 gigajoules per car. That's the equivalent of 9,445kWh of electricity, or about 1.5 tonnes of coal.

WHAT WOULD YOU SEE IF YOU WERE TRAVELLING AT THE SPEED OF LIGHT?

Einstein asked himself this very question when he was 16 and his search for a solution led him to the Special Theory of Relativity. According to this, the speed of light is a universal constant and thus the same for all observers. That, in turn, implies that lengths and time intervals aren't absolute, but vary according to how objects move relative to one another, so as to ensure that measurements of the speed of light always give the same result.

Following Einstein's publication of these astounding insights in 1905, a debate broke out over the resulting visual impact of these effects. The arguments centred on whether the predicted effects - such as length contraction - could be observed, given that both the effect itself and any attempt to observe it are affected by the speed of light. Definitive answers took decades to emerge, but they show that the shape, brightness and colour of objects are all affected. For example, an observer moving at near light-speed down a street would see the buildings on either side curl up to create the impression of flying down a tube. The view ahead, meanwhile, would appear brilliantly white, while to the rear everything would vanish into darkness.

WHY DO PLANES APPEAR TO TRAVEL SO SLOWLY IN THE SKY?

Our brains judge the speed of objects passing by us through the time taken for them to cross our field of view. Those taking a long time could either be nearby and travelling slowly or faster and further away. And in the case of planes, our brains know that the second interpretation is the right one.

CAN AN AIRCRAFT AUTOPILOT FLY THE ENTIRE ROUTE?

The autopilot on an aircraft can fly the whole route apart from take-off. Once airborne, the plane can climb automatically, cruise and then descend all the way to the runway. But 'autoland' is only used when visibility is too poor for a visual approach. Autopilots lock onto a runway's Instrument Landing System (ILS). The ILS is a radio beam coning upward from the ground, forming an invisible tunnel down which the plane flies.

After take-off, some flight crew engage the autopilot from about 1,000ft, whereas others prefer to fly manually almost all the way to the cruise. After levelling out, the autopilot is usually engaged because otherwise it is hard work keeping a plane straight and level for hours on end. Most autopilots handle turbulence quite well, but if it gets really bumpy, the crew might choose to ride it out with the manual flight controls.

THINKSTOCK, ALAMY X2, GETTY IMAGES/POLKA DOT RF, AIRBUS

COULD WE EVER FUEL CARS WITH GRASS?

The cellulose that makes up grass can be chemically fermented to produce alcohol, which could propel vehicles. While the economics of growing and converting it don't add up, they just might for special types of grass, such as so-called switchgrass, *Panicum virgatum*, which is prevalent in North America.

WHY DO MANY PLANES HAVE TIPPED WINGS?

The structures that sweep upwards on aircraft wings are called winglets. Wings have a curved cross-section and lift is formed by the pressure difference between the air flowing over the top and that underneath. Air travels faster over the curved top and thus is lower in pressure than on the underside. But at the tips, air from underneath tries to flow up and over the wing, reducing lift. The winglet blocks that effect and reduces drag by preventing vortices from forming as the tapered wingtips cut through the air. Planes like the Airbus A320 have winglets. They are also common on business jets: increased lift allows a shorter take-off, enabling the jets to get in and out of smaller airfields.

WHAT IS A BLACK BOX RECORDER MADE OF?

Let's start by dispelling one myth. Flight data recorders are not black, but coloured bright orange so that they can be found easily after an aviation accident. Aircraft carry two black boxes. The flight data recorder continuously logs details like the plane's speed, altitude, time of day and engine parameters. The other unit records the pilots' voices in the cockpit.

The units need to be resistant to fire and water, and to be able to cope with the force of a major impact. They also need to withstand low air pressures at altitude should the aircraft suffer a sudden decompression. Likewise, the recorder should be capable of bearing the crushing pressures down on the seafloor should the aircraft plunge into the ocean.

As a result, black boxes require very strong casings. Earlier models were simply made from stainless steel, but now housings also incorporate titanium, as well as an inner layer of heat-resistant material.

WHAT'S THE FASTEST HELICOPTER IN THE WORLD?

Officially, the world's fastest chopper is the Westland Lynx, a multi-purpose military aircraft that has seen naval and battlefield use. In its record-breaking flight in 1987, a Lynx helicopter flew a 15km course in Somerset near the Yeovil factory where it was manufactured. Over two legs, the aircraft managed an average of 400km/h.

However in July 2010, the Sikorsky X2 helicopter beat the Lynx, achieving 417km/h in a test flight. The Sikorsky is a distinctive beast with an inverted tail and coaxial rotors. There are two rotors, each with four blades mounted one above the other, rotating in opposite directions. There is also a six-bladed propeller at the rear. This configuration is designed to increase speed and to usher in the next generation of super-fast military and civil helicopters. However, there was no observer from the National Aeronautic Association to witness the Sikorsky flight, so the Lynx's record still stands.

AP/PRESS ASSOCIATION IMAGES, AUGUSTA WESTLAND, THINKSTOCK

WHAT'S THE WORLD'S FASTEST TRAIN?

The fastest operational passenger service is China's Shanghai Transrapid maglev line. It hurtles passengers to and from Pudong International Airport at up to 483km/h (300 miles per hour). Maglev trains are propelled by giant magnets in the track and 'levitate' above the track. In a test run, the Transrapid managed 501km/h (311 miles per hour). However, that record was beaten in August 2013 by Central Japan Railway Company's prototype L0 series maglev train. It managed 504 km/h (313mph). Unlike the Transrapid, the L0 is not carrying passengers yet, but will eventually service parts of the route between Tokyo and Osaka. Hundreds of kilometres of tunnels need digging and the first section is not due to open until 2027.

DID YOU KNOW?

The largest land vehicle is the 14,196-tonne TAKRAF RB293 bucket-wheel excavator. Built in 1995, the 220m long vehicle moves earth in a German coalmine.

WHAT IS THE OXYGEN LEVEL IN A PLANE?

Oxygen levels in flight are broadly the same as on the ground, about 210,000 parts per million by volume. However, at cruise altitude the cabin pressure is lower than on the ground at around 82kPa, equivalent to about 1,800m (6,000ft). For comparison, air pressure at sea level is 101kPa. At this low pressure, oxygen levels in the blood are lower than at sea level. A healthy person suffers no effects, but those with respiratory illnesses sometimes need additional oxygen.

How do you calculate the effect of cosmic radiation on cloud formation?

One hundred metres below the ground, the CLOUD (Cosmics Leaving Outdoor Droplets) experiment unfolds. This is the top of the cloud chamber where beams of ionising particles, tuned to mimic the cosmic radiation that rains relentlessly down on Earth, are fired through plumes of atmospheric gases. The experiment is investigating the effect of cosmic radiation on cloud formation, an important factor in understanding the Sun's role in climate change.

To mimic atmospheric conditions, the chamber must be kept as free from impurities as possible. "We're the only cloud chamber in the world that can do these experiments at the required level of cleanliness," said CLOUD spokesperson Jasper Kirkby. "It's a big subject, but we'll answer the question definitively in about 10 years."

So far, CLOUD has blasted high-energy particles at amines, derivatives of ammonia. Next up will be sweet-smelling monoterpenes. "When you go into the forest, that lovely smell is the monoterpenes. They're organic compounds with a lot of carbon in them and we will try to understand how they interact with cosmic radiation."

The experiment is at CERN, the European nuclear research facility located in France and Switzerland.

For more great pictures, follow us on http://pinterest.com/sciencefocus

CERN

THE HOME

Drugs, germs and shrinking clothes – our homes are a maze of puzzles and conundrums. You might be surprised by some of the answers...

WHEN WILL WE SEE THE END OF COMPUTER KEYBOARDS?

It's impossible to say when, if ever, we're going to kill off the QWERTY keyboard. But other technologies are typing out its death warrant. Many of us are already using touch-and-swipe devices like tablets. In 2011, Microsoft Research and Carnegie Mellon University developed a system called 'OmniTouch' (pictured). It combines picoprojectors and movement-tracking software that will allow you to project virtual keypads on to any surface, even your hand.

WHY DO ELECTRONIC GADGETS USE SEMICONDUCTORS?

Every electronic gadget needs to be able to control the flow of electric current rapidly and precisely, but without needing bulky switches or valves. The beauty of semiconductors like silicon is that – unlike metals such as copper – they can be changed from conductors of electricity into insulators by applying a small voltage. This allows them to act like tiny switches, whose on or off state can be used for a host of functions, including calculations.

HOW DOES A KNIFE CUT?

Imagine squashing a block of butter with the palm of your hand. The butter has to move out of the way, so it is squeezed sideways as it gets flattened. Now use the edge of your hand, like a slow-motion karate chop. The edge has much less surface area, so the pressure is higher and it is easier to push your hand through. Also, because the edge is narrower, you don't need to push so much of the butter out of the way. Instead of flattening the whole block, you leave a narrow slot.

The blade of a knife is like a very thin hand. It applies huge pressure at the edge to push the material apart. When you try to cut a tomato, a blunt knife crushes a wide band of plant cells underneath it, but a sharp knife will cut through a single line of cells, separating the long-chain cellulose molecules in the cell wall.

The sharpest knives are those with the thinnest edges. Obsidian (a form of glass) can be sharpened to an edge just three atoms across. Obsidian scalpels are sometimes used in surgery and have been found to produce less scarring, but a narrow edge is more delicate and the obsidian blades become blunt more quickly than surgical steel.

CAN YOU 'BANK' SLEEP IN ADVANCE?

To a limited extent, yes. A 1991 study at Wright State University in Dayton, Ohio found that after an ordinary night's sleep, subjects could take an extra nap in the afternoon and then work through the night with greater alertness than a control group who didn't nap. The study also found that performance was proportional to the length of the nap – but the effect doesn't last. After a second consecutive night without sleep, all of the subjects performed equally badly, regardless of how much sleep they had initially. It may be that all of us are normally slightly sleep-deprived and that one really good night's sleep will bring us back up to 100 per cent, but that the 'tank' isn't big enough to buffer us against more than one all-nighter.

WHY DO WE EAT SAVOURY BEFORE SWEET AT MEALS?

We have evolved a preference for sweet tastes for two reasons: sugar is a high-energy food source, and it is also quite rare in nature. Honey, fruit and the sap from certain plants are the only accessible forms of relatively pure sugar and, before they were cultivated by humans, most fruits were a lot less sweet than they are today. A sweet tooth is therefore an evolutionary advantage, because it encourages you to seek out these energy-giving calorific foodstuffs.

In the Middle Ages, most people didn't eat meals in separate courses; fruit and meat were mixed together in lots of dishes. But refined sugar was so expensive that it was reserved for the nobility. The main meal was eaten with the servants and after it had been cleared away, the lord and lady might retire to their private rooms for a second course of luxurious sweet dishes. The word 'dessert' comes from the Old French *desservir*, meaning 'to clear the table'.

HOW DO SAFETY MATCHES WORK?

The 'strike anywhere' variety of match is basically Armstrong's mixture. This is an explosive made of red phosphorus, with potassium chlorate as an oxidiser. Armstrong's mixture is so reactive that even a small bump will set it off (very small amounts are used in the paper caps for toy guns), so matches have various binders and fillers added to stop the box igniting when you shake it. But still, the friction of the match head against sandpaper or another rough surface is enough to trigger the reaction. Safety matches work by separating the two main ingredients. The red phosphorus is on the striking surface of the box, while the match head contains the potassium chlorate. When they are rubbed together, the friction causes a tiny reaction at the point of contact and, after that, sulphur and starch in the match head burn to sustain the flame.

THINKSTOCK X3, ALAMY X2

WHY DO MOTHS EAT CLOTHES?

The adult clothes moth *Tineola bisselliella* doesn't eat at all. But its larvae do and they can digest the protein keratin that is found in wool, silk and leather. The larvae can't drink water directly and need a food source that contains moisture: wool is particularly good for this, and a dark wardrobe is an ideal spot. After about two months, they pupate into the adult form, fly off to find a mate and repeat the cycle.

IS IT MORE HYGIENIC TO USE A PLASTIC CHOPPING BOARD OR A WOODEN ONE?

Wood is slightly better. A new plastic chopping board is easy to clean, but a sharp knife creates shallow cuts in the surface that can trap bacteria. Putting it in the dishwasher is enough to clean it properly, but the lower temperatures of a hand wash won't kill the bacteria. Wooden chopping boards trap bacteria in cuts as well, but research at the University of California, Davis showed that the bacteria do not multiply in the wood.

HOW DOES PARACETAMOL GET RID OF HEADACHES?

The exact mechanism is still not well understood, but it seems that paracetamol does at least two different things. One is to inhibit the action of the cyclo-oxygenase family of enzymes, which are involved with the body's inflammatory response. Inflammation can be a useful part of the healing process, but in an ordinary headache, it's just a source of pain.

Paracetamol also affects a series of biochemical pathways called the endogenous cannabinoid system. This is involved with controlling appetite and our sensitivity to pain. Paracetamol blocks the re-uptake of a key neurotransmitter and thereby lowers our sensitivity to pain.

TOP TEN

DRUGS DISPENSED IN THE UK

(Source: Health and social care information centre, 2012)

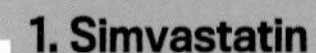

1. Simvastatin
Number dispensed: 42.6 million
Use: Lowers cholesterol to control heart disease

2. Aspirin
Number dispensed: 31.7 million
Use: Painkiller, fever reduction and anti-inflammatory

3. Levothryroxine sodium
Number dispensed: 26.7 million
Use: Treatment of thyroid deficiency and cancers

4. Omeprazole
Number dispensed: 25.8 million
Use: Inhibits gastric secretion and protects the stomach lining

5. Ramipril
Number dispensed: 23.8 million
Use: Treats high blood pressure and heart failure

6. Paracetamol
Number dispensed: 21.9 million
Use: Painkiller

7. Amlodipine
Number dispensed: 21.6 million
Use: Calcium-channel blocker - used to treat angina

8. Salbutamol
Number dispensed: 20.5 million
Use: Makes breathing easier by widening the airways (bronchi)

9. Lansoprazole
Number dispensed: 19 million
Use: Inhibits gastric secretion and protects the stomach lining

10. Bendroflumethiazide
Number dispensed: 17.3 million
Use: Diuretic

WHICH IS BETTER FOR YOU - COLA OR DIET COLA?

The main difference is obviously that cola contains sugar and diet cola contains artificial sweetener. In the UK, that sweetener is aspartame and the current scientific consensus is that this additive is safe at the concentrations found in diet drinks. The 35g of sugar - around seven teaspoons - in a can of cola, on the other hand, contains 139 calories, which will contribute to obesity and tooth decay. It can also lead to Type II diabetes if you drink too much of it. On balance, diet cola is probably the least bad, but neither is actually good for you.

DOES ASPARAGUS HELP A HANGOVER?

While alcohol in your blood can make you feel good, the breakdown products give you a hangover. When you drink alcohol (ethanol), the enzyme alcohol dehydrogenase in your liver converts it to acetaldehyde (ethanal). This acetaldehyde dehydrogenase takes over and turns the ethanal to acetate, before it's broken down into carbon dioxide and water.

Asparagus contains compounds that more than double the speed of both the alcohol and acetaldehyde dehydrogenase enzymes. If you ate asparagus the morning after drinking, it would help to mop up any remaining ethanal in your blood. The downside is that a bottleneck is created that will increase the levels of acetate. This causes the chemical adenosine to accumulate in your brain, which lowers the activity of your brain cells. This is why a hangover also makes you feel sluggish. Luckily, caffeine binds to the same receptors as adenosine, so a cup of coffee prevents the adenosine from slowing you down.

THINKSTOCK X8, ALAMY

WHAT'S THE HIGHEST ENERGY FOOD?

The Ultimate Breakfast Platter, from Burger King's menu in the US, has 1,450 calories and topped a recent poll that compared calories per dollar for 10 US fast-food chains.

However, for a single, unprocessed food, it's hard to top the almond. They are often cited as one of the highest-energy single foodstuffs. A report by the Institute of Food Technologists stated that foods with smaller particle sizes are absorbed better, so almond butter ought to have the most calories per hundred grammes. In fact, it's about the same as peanut butter at 620kcal/100g. Ordinary butter is slightly higher (740kcal/100g), but pure sunflower oil beats both at 900kcal/100g.

IS GREEN TEA BETTER FOR YOU THAN BREAKFAST TEA?

All tea contains antioxidant compounds called catechins. Black tea involves oxidising the leaves more so than green, and so black tea is slightly less antioxidant. Studies have shown health benefits for both kinds of tea, including reduced blood cholesterol and lower rates of cardiovascular disease, but green tea seems to have the edge. This may be partly because it's drunk without milk. Drinking black tea with milk has no cardiovascular benefit, according to a 2006 study at Berlin University. In addition, a 2012 study in China found that green tea also repairs age-related damage to brain cells.

HOW DO BATH BOMBS WORK?

The part that makes them fizz is the same as in a soluble aspirin tablet: sodium bicarbonate and citric acid. These chemicals are inert when they are dry powders, but in water they dissolve and the citric acid reacts with the sodium bicarbonate to form sodium citrate and carbon dioxide. The sodium citrate stays in solution and you don't really notice it, but the carbon dioxide bubbles out as a gas that helps the bath bomb break up. This lets the detergents, perfumes and oils that make up the rest of the bath bomb mix with the bathwater.

HOW DOES THE DYSON BLADELESS FAN WORK?

The Dyson fan has blades inside its base that draw in about 27 litres of air per second and pass it through the circular tube mounted on top. In the rim of the tube is a thin foil that sucks in more air. This creates a multiplier effect, with more and more air passing through the ring. The effect is boosted by a process called 'entrainment', whereby air near the edges of the fan is also swept into the stream. The result is a device that creates, Dyson claims, an air output 15 times that of a conventional fan.

HOW DOES AN ANTI-SNORE PILLOW WORK?

Snoring is caused by the soft palate vibrating as it partially blocks the airway. Anti-snoring pillows tilt the head backwards as you lie on your back. It's similar to the way that you tilt the patient's head during cardiopulmonary resuscitation (CPR), helping to hold the airway open.

PA ARCHIVE/PRESS ASSOCIATION IMAGES, THINKSTOCK X2, ALAMY

IS GLASSWARE MORE FRAGILE WHEN HOT?

It's not high temperatures that are the problem; it's *uneven* temperatures. If you put a glass in the fridge, chill it down to 4°C and then pour boiling water into it, the bottom of the glass heats up by 100°C. But glass is a good insulator, so it takes several seconds for the heat to spread to the rim. That 96°C difference causes the circumference of the base to expand by about 0.18mm, while the rim stays the same. That doesn't sound like much, but glass is very brittle, so the sudden stress is enough to crack it.

DID YOU KNOW?

The teabag was invented by accident: in 1908 they were sent out as samples and customers wrongly assumed they had to put the entire bag in the pot, rather than emptying out the contents.

HOW DOES A WHISTLING KETTLE WHISTLE?

Most kettle whistles consist of two parallel metal plates with a hole running through them through which steam passes. The whistling sound is the result of this flow of steam making the air vibrate rapidly, but only now have researchers worked out how.

According to Ross Henrywood and Dr Anurag Agarwal at the University of Cambridge, there are two mechanisms at work. The first, known as Helmholtz resonance, occurs when the steam tries to push out of the whistle, only to run into the natural 'springiness' of air still in it. The resulting vibrations produce the first sounds from the whistle. But as the steam gets hotter, it pushes through the holes in the whistle faster, creating ripples of turbulence, and these generate the final note.

WHICH HARBOUR MORE GERMS - TOUCH SCREENS OR KEYBOARDS?

It's been dubbed 'QWERTY tummy'. Yes, the bad news is that one of the most widespread bugs found on computer keyboards is *Staphylococcus aureus*, a bacterium that causes food poisoning. That and other harmful germs are transferred onto our keyboards after we have been to the loo, eaten lunch at our desk or picked our nose.

A study in 2008 found that some keyboards were dirtier than a toilet seat. The news is no better when it comes to the screens on our phones. Two years ago, a study from the London School of Hygiene & Tropical Medicine and Queen Mary University of London found that 92 per cent of phones harboured bacteria despite 95 per cent of users saying they washed their hands thoroughly. One in six handsets were contaminated with *Escherichia coli* bacteria, the type that leads to severe food poisoning.

Whether touch screens are grubbier than keyboards or vice versa is tricky to determine. Given that we tend to take our phones and tablets everywhere, sometimes even to the loo, I would say that touching transfers more toxins than typing. A pack of anti-bacterial hand wipes should do the trick.

45

The number of years between the first patented design of tin cans by Peter Durand in 1810 and the invention of a tin opener, in 1855, by Robert Yates.

WHY DO CLOTHES SHRINK IN THE WASH?

Wool is prone to this because animal hairs are made of keratin scales that overlap each other like tiles on a roof. When a jumper is heated and wetted, the fibres are jostled past each other and the pattern of the scales causes them to ratchet in one direction. So the individual strands of yarn tighten up.

Other fabrics shrink because the fibres get stretched during spinning and weaving, and this tension gets locked into the final garment. Heat and water loosen them and allow them to relax back to their original length before they became garments.

ALAMY X2, THINKSTOCK X2

IS THERE ANY FOOD THAT HELPS YOU BURN FAT?

The whole idea of fat-burning foods is just a marketing ploy used by supplement manufacturers to sell the idea that you can somehow take short-cuts to weight loss. There is some research (such as a 2012 study in the *Journal of the American Medical Association*) to suggest that you burn slightly more calories each day on a low-glycemic index diet than one which involves lots of sugar and refined carbohydrate. But you still won't 'burn fat' unless you use more calories than you eat.

WHICH HAS MORE HEALTH BENEFITS: DRINKING HOT WATER OR COLD?

Mostly it makes no difference. Any water that you drink will be absorbed by the intestines regardless of its starting temperature. If it wasn't absorbed, it would give you diarrhoea. Hot or cold drinks obviously have a temporary effect on your body temperature, but which one is better will depend on whether you need warming up or cooling down. There is however some research to show that a hot drink is better for you when you have a cold. Studies as far back as 1979 found that the steam from a hot drink increases the 'nasal mucus velocity'. As horrible as that sounds, runnier mucus is better because it stops the nose from blocking up altogether, which can lead to a secondary sinus infection. Chicken soup works even better, because the aroma of the soup increases the blood flow to your nostrils.

ALMA (ESO/NAOJ/NRAO)/VISIBLE LIGHT IMAGE: THE NASA/ESA HUBBLE SPACE TELESCOPE

Which galaxy is this?

This collection of stars and gases is actually two colliding galaxies. The Antennae Galaxies, which are 45 million light-years away, are slowly joining to become one giant galaxy. They can be seen as never before thanks to a new telescope facility in northern Chile, the Atacama Large Millimeter/sub-millimeter Array, or ALMA for short.

Most of this image – the first ALMA has taken – was created with just 12 of the 66 radio antennas that will eventually make up the array. The antennas detect much longer wavelengths than visible light. "The ALMA data is in red and yellow," says Dr Leonardo Testi, an ALMA project scientist. "In both cases, this is interstellar gas and is where we think stars are forming." The other part of this composite image (in blue) was taken by the Hubble Space Telescope using visible light and shows stars within the galaxies.

For more great pictures, follow us on http://pinterest.com/sciencefocus

ENERGY & ENVIRONMENT

The environment we live in is ever-changing, partly due to natural causes and partly as a result of human actions. The result is a plethora of new mysteries and discoveries

WHAT IS A ROGUE WAVE?

It's a wave that's twice as high as the highest wave normally seen under a given set of conditions. Rogue waves have been part of sailing folklore for centuries, but their existence was only proven in 1995 when a 25m wave was recorded in the North Sea. Any ship encountering such a steep wave would be snapped in half, but rogue waves are very rare. The 1978 sinking of the MS München, attributed at the time to severe weather, is the only confirmed case.

DO HOUSEHOLD CLEANING PRODUCTS AFFECT THE ENVIRONMENT?

From detergents to bug-killing bleach, we use a lot of pretty nasty chemicals in the home, much of which can end up entering the environment via the drains. Yet the notorious 'detergent foam' seen in rivers and streams is usually the result of entirely natural bacterial action on decaying vegetation, whose cells break down to produce so-called surfactants that foam up easily. As for bleach, studies have shown that it rapidly breaks down in the environment, posing no serious hazard.

WHERE DOES THE LIGHT GO WHEN YOU TURN OFF THE SWITCH?

Light isn't like a cloud of fog that hangs in the air; it's a continuous stream of photons emitted from the light bulb in the middle of the room. Each photon travels in a straight line and a couple of nanoseconds later it reaches the wall.

There it might be absorbed by one of the electrons in an atom in the wall, which makes the atom vibrate a little faster and so the wall heats up slightly. Or it might be re-emitted at the same or a different wavelength.

While the light is switched on, this process is occurring continuously, with a small fraction of the re-emitted photons ending up in your eye, where they are absorbed by the atoms of your retina and cause you to perceive the room as lit. When the light goes out, no new photons are emitted and the existing ones bounce around a couple of times until all of them have been absorbed.

Even if the walls of the room were mirrors, the light would vanish almost immediately because no mirror is a perfect reflector and light travels so fast that it bounces off the opposite walls millions of times a second. Even a 99.9 per cent perfect mirror would absorb all the leftover photons in a microsecond or so.

DOES ICE CONDUCT ELECTRICITY?

To conduct electricity, a substance must be able to allow carriers of electric charges to move within it; only then will the charges start to flow, creating a current when a voltage is applied. While liquid water is a fairly poor conductor of electricity, ice is even worse because of its low temperature and rigid crystal structure.

CAN HUMAN ACTIONS CAUSE EARTHQUAKES?

This question was at the centre of the controversy over tremors reportedly caused by the extraction of shale gas from a site near Blackpool in 2011. There's no doubt that human activity can trigger quakes: nuclear tests, hydroelectric dams and coal mining have all been linked with tremors. The key issue is how big these tremors are – and whether they would happen anyway.

When the US conducted its largest-ever nuclear test off Alaska in November 1971, it unleashed the same seismic energy as an earthquake measuring magnitude 7 on the Richter scale. Yet despite its violence, the explosion only triggered some minor natural tremors of the type routinely felt in the region. It's the same with mining and drilling (and the fracking operations near Blackpool). They can trigger small natural tremors but not a full-blown earthquake.

WHAT'S THE 'ENERGY HARVESTING DANCEFLOOR'?

This sustainable dancefloor was first deployed in a nightclub in Rotterdam. It consists of panels that flex slightly as you dance. This movement converts your gyrations into electricity due to something called the piezoelectric effect. Each panel is about the surface area of a large carpet tile and can produce up to 35W, powering in-built LED disco lights. Portable versions are available too; one was shipped to Vancouver for the 2010 Winter Olympics.

WHY CAN'T WE BURY NUCLEAR WASTE IN A SUBDUCTION ZONE?

Subduction zones occur where one vast slab of Earth's crust slips below another and into the 2,000°C-plus regions below. As such, they sound ideal for disposal of radioactive waste, arguably the biggest problem facing the wider use of nuclear power.

The idea is beset by a host of problems, however. The most obvious is that suitable subduction zones would be far from any land, deep below the sea, and thus tricky to access reliably. In any case, such 'out of sight, out of mind' disposal at sea is currently banned. The law could be changed if a strong enough scientific case could be made, but this is unlikely. Subduction zones are geologically highly unstable and are the site of some of the world's most powerful earthquakes. This raises the possibility of the waste containers being damaged and driven back onto the sea-bed, rather than incinerated in the depths of Earth.

These risks, along with the problems of simply getting to the dumping sites, have been assessed by scientists from nations faced with the problem of nuclear waste disposal, including the UK Committee on Radioactive Waste Management. And to date all have ruled out the idea.

HOW DOES SEA FOG FORM?

Fog is just cloud that touches Earth's surface and it forms the same way that clouds do. Water in the vapour state is transparent and invisible. The warmer the air, the more kinetic energy it has and so the more water molecules it can keep jostling around as vapour.

If warm air with lots of water vapour in it cools down suddenly, the water molecules slow down too much to stay as vapour. Instead they clump together into tiny droplets of liquid water. The droplets are still small enough to hang suspended in the air currents, but now they appear opaque because light reflects off the air/water interface.

Sea fog can occur when warm wet air rolls off the land and onto the colder sea, or when a warm weather front hits a cold ocean current. In the UK, the north-east coast is very prone to sea fog because of the cold waters of the North Sea.

ROBIN UTRECHT/EPA/CORBIS, ALAMY, THINKSTOCK X2

WHAT IS THE MOST POWERFUL NUCLEAR BOMB EVER DETONATED?

On 30 October 1961, the Soviet Union tested the AN602 thermonuclear bomb, nicknamed the 'Tsar Bomb', over Novaya Zemlya north of the Arctic Circle. The nuclear fusion-powered explosion was equivalent to over 50 million tonnes of TNT, over a 1,000 times more devastating than the atomic bombs dropped on Japan in 1945.

DID YOU KNOW?

The air around a lightning strike is the hottest place on Earth. For a split second, temperatures hit 30,000°C, hotter than the surface of the Sun.

HOW MUCH POWER DO THE BIGGEST CITIES USE?

London, with a population of around eight million, uses electrical power at an average rate equivalent to the output of around five nuclear power stations. But size isn't everything. Dubai, where temperatures regularly reach over 40°C, is home to some of the most power-hungry people in the world. They consume it at a rate equivalent to the output of four nuclear power stations – while having barely one-quarter the population of London.

400,000

tonnes of carbon dioxide is pulled from the atmosphere each year as a result of iron-rich whale poo, stimulating the growth of plankton that feast on the greenhouse gas.

HOW LONG DOES IT TAKE STALAGMITES AND STALACTITES TO FORM?

Stalactites form when water containing dissolved calcium bicarbonate from the limestone rock drips from the ceiling of a cave. As the water comes into contact with the air, some of the calcium bicarbonate precipitates back into limestone to form a tiny ring, which gradually elongates to form a stalactite.

Stalagmites grow upwards from the drips that fall to the floor. They spread outwards more, so they have a wider, flatter shape than stalactites, but they gain mass at roughly the same rate. Limestone stalactites form extremely slowly – usually less than 10cm every thousand years – and radiometric dating has shown that some are over 190,000 years old.

Stalactites can also form by a different chemical process when water drips through concrete and this is much faster. Stalactites under concrete bridges can grow as fast as a centimetre per year.

THINKSTOCK X2, ALAMY

HOW ARE OIL SPILLS CLEANED UP?

Over the years, everything from steam and chemical sprays to igniting the oil has been tried, with sometimes disastrous consequences. In 1967, the oil supertanker Torrey Canyon was holed off Land's End, triggering the world's first attempt at a major clean-up. Detergents were tried as a means of breaking up the oil slick, while aircraft attempted to burn it off by bombing it with napalm. It did not work well: a lot of marine life was either incinerated or poisoned by the chemicals.

In 1989, the Exxon Valdez disaster in Prince William Sound, Alaska saw the use of high-pressure steam cleaning of the affected area. This made the coastline look clean, but sent oil down into areas previously untouched, while scalding to death microscopic marine life.

A host of techniques have been used in the aftermath of BP's Deepwater Horizon oil-rig disaster in the Gulf of Mexico in 2010, from the latest generation of dispersants to simply sucking the stuff up onto specially modified ships. But the same problems have emerged. Studies suggest the dispersants are proving much more toxic than the method that may prove best in the long run: leaving nature to it.

WHAT'S THE SINGLE LARGEST THREAT TO HUMANITY?

The human species is resourceful, adaptable, numerous and very widely dispersed around the globe. To render us entirely extinct would require a very sudden, planet-wide catastrophe. Gradual climate change of the sort that has been responsible for mass extinctions in the past wouldn't do it, because we would have time to find technological solutions that would save at least some of the species.

Global thermonuclear war, an impact from a meteorite larger than 10km, a sudden supervolcano eruption or an incredibly contagious and virulent disease are the only real candidates with the ability to kill enough of us, fast enough. None of them are at all likely and deciding which is the least unlikely is very difficult.

Genetic analysis has suggested that the global population may have fallen to less than 15,000 after the Toba supervolcano erupted 70,000 years ago. If a Stone Age civilisation was able to recover from a population crash like that, then the outlook for our species now is probably quite rosy.

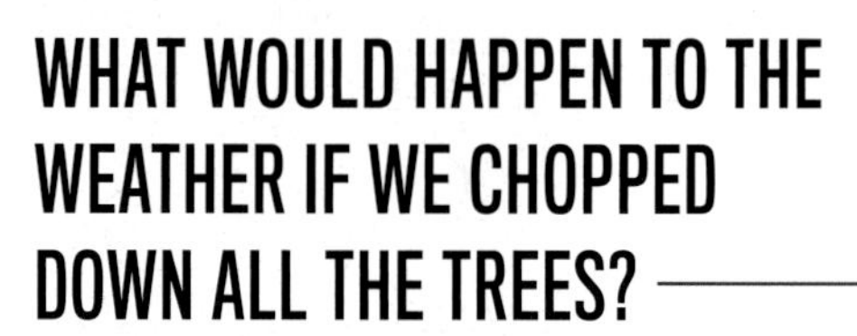

WHAT WOULD HAPPEN TO THE WEATHER IF WE CHOPPED DOWN ALL THE TREES?

In the UK, there are about 150 million tonnes of carbon locked up in trees. Cutting them down and burning them would result in roughly the same amount of CO_2 that the UK emits in a year. Deforestation globally currently contributes about 15 per cent of greenhouse gas emissions.

Trees play an important role in taking water from the ground and releasing it into the atmosphere. Without trees, more rainwater would stay locked underground or run off into the sea, reducing the amount of evaporation from the land. The soil erosion that occurs without tree roots to stabilise the ground would also lead to an expansion of the desert regions and, overall, the climate would probably become windier, warmer and drier. The exact effect on the local climate in the UK could be hard to predict though. If weather systems like the Gulf Stream were disrupted, the UK could actually get much colder.

ALAMY X2, THINKSTOCK X6

CAN WAVES FREEZE?

Even in Antarctic conditions, it just isn't possible to extract energy fast enough from a solid mass of water to freeze a moving wave in one go. But just as icicles can form from repeated drips, multiple waves breaking on a cold shore can leave a thin crust of ice that gradually builds up into a jagged arrangement of ice shards that resembles a single frozen wave.

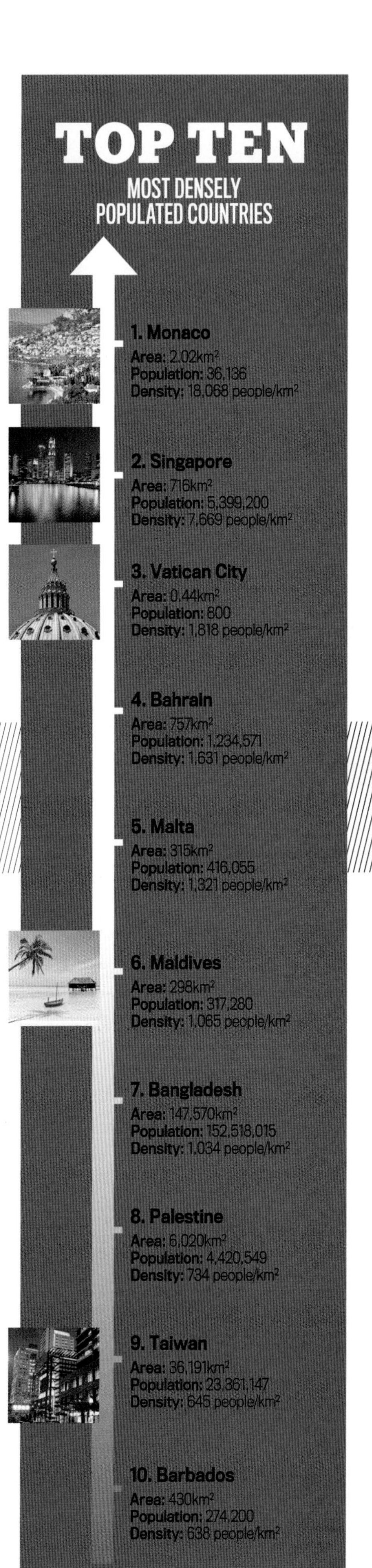

What is a sea angel?

This largely translucent undersea creature is something of an enigma: for much of the year, no-one knows where it lives. The sea angel, *Clione limacina*, predominantly inhabits the icy waters near the North Pole (although this one came from just outside the Arctic Circle, in the White Sea in northern Russia). It makes its appearance in spring at the same time as its only food source, the sea butterfly. "For a few weeks, sea angels hunt sea butterflies, which all at once practically disappear," says marine biologist Alexander Semenov at Moscow State University. "A couple of weeks later, the angels disappear too. But no-one knows where they go."

Sea angels grow up to 5cm in length and their wings allow them to swim much faster than sea butterflies, whose wings are less effective. The predator clasps its prey with its tentacles, rotating it until its shell opening is in the right position for hooks to be inserted. These hooks are then used to draw the hapless creature out before swallowing it whole.

For more great pictures, follow us on http://pinterest.com/sciencefocus

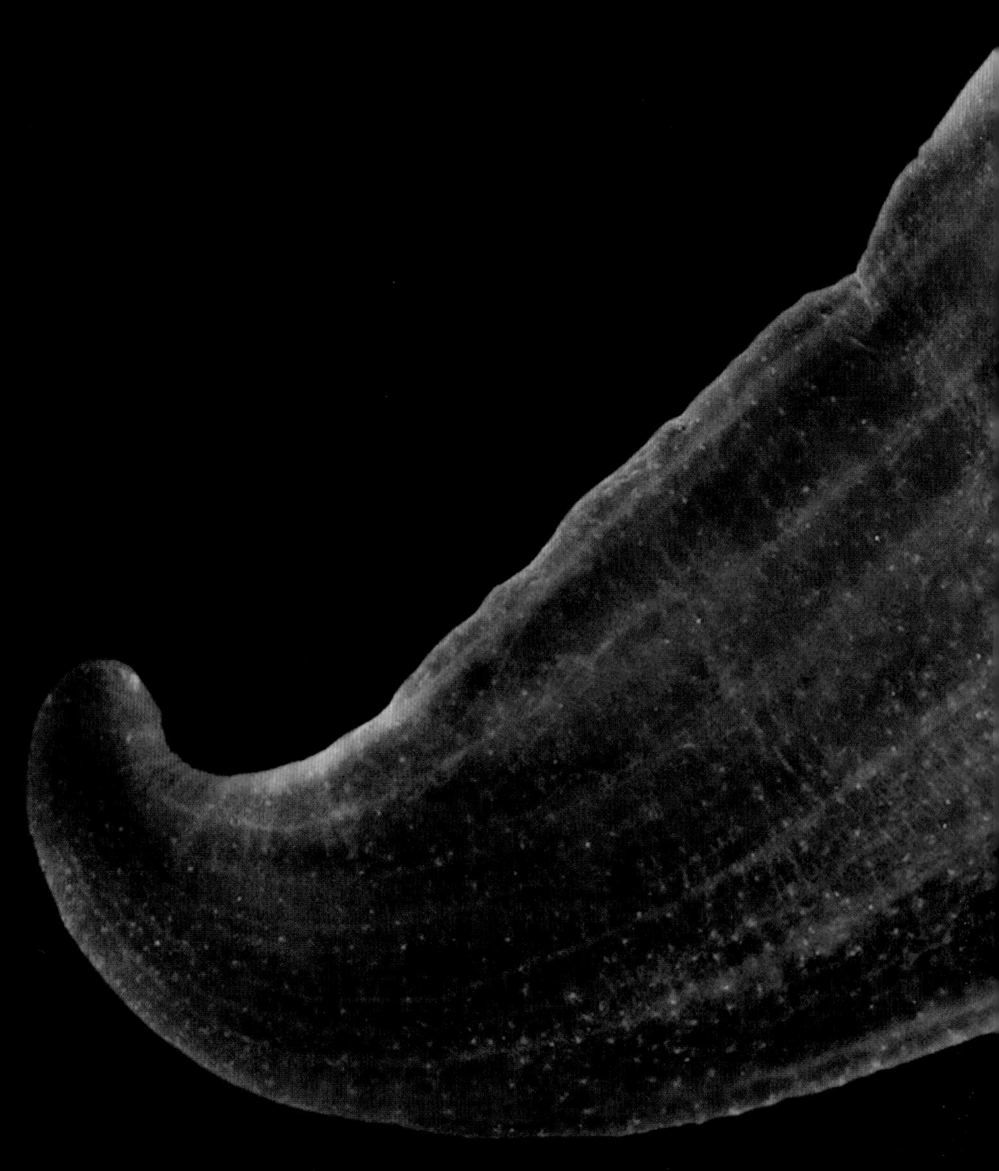

ALEXANDER SEMENOV

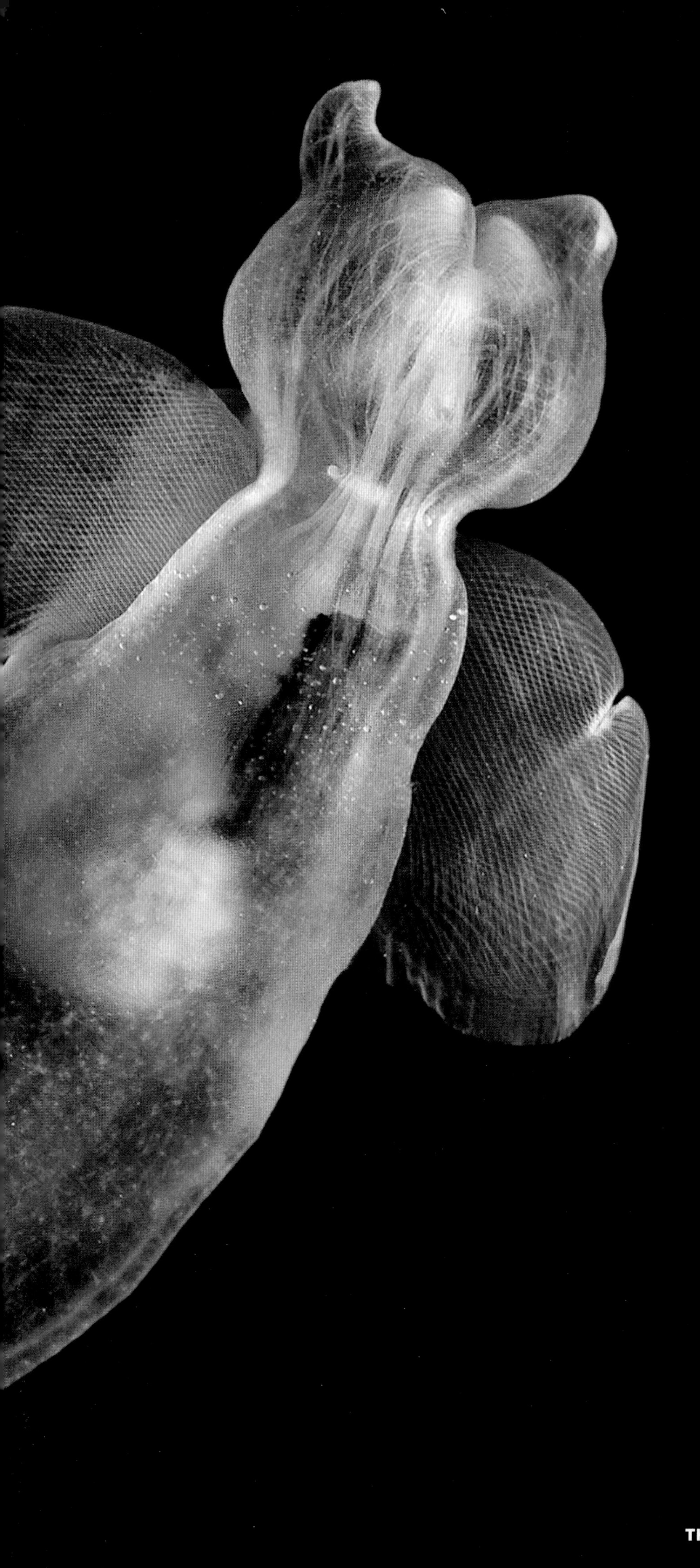

HOW IT WORKS

A BLU-RAY DISC

You might have enjoyed the high-definition (HD) quality of Blu-ray films such as *Avatar* on a big TV. If not, you're missing out. Blu-ray discs were designed to replace DVD, with a higher capacity for data enabling HD video. The name Blu-ray is derived from the blue laser used to read the disc. This allows data to be stored at a higher density than is possible with the longer wavelength red lasers used for DVD and CD.

The information density of the DVD format was limited by the wavelength of the lasers used. Following the development of new technology, primarily at Sony, blue lasers operating at 405 nanometres (nm) became available, replacing the 650nm red lasers used in DVD players. This means that more information about a film can be stored on a disc, leading to crisper, more detailed footage.

CD

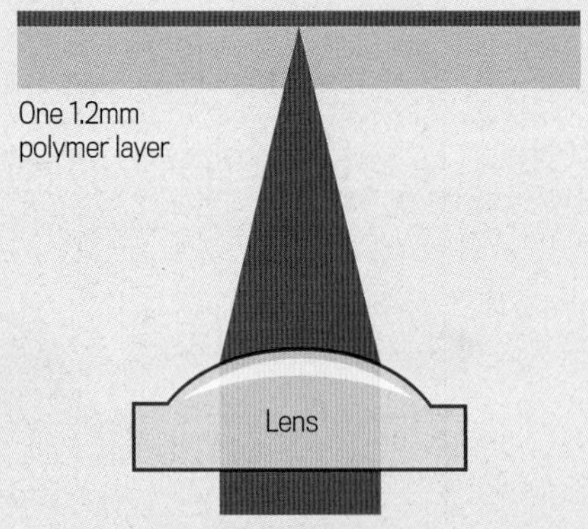

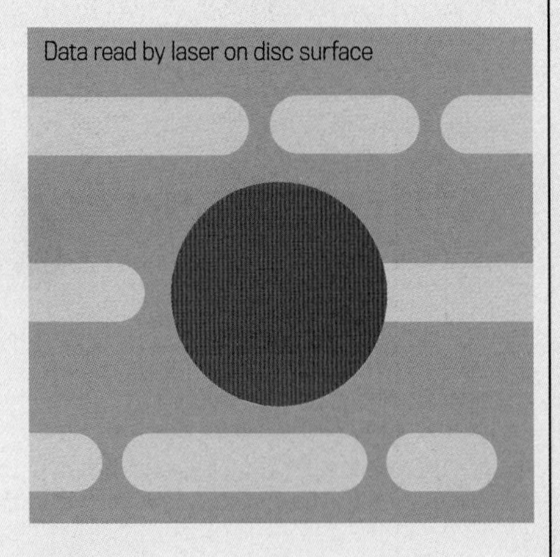

CAPACITY

0.7GB

Over 200 billion CDs have been sold

DVD

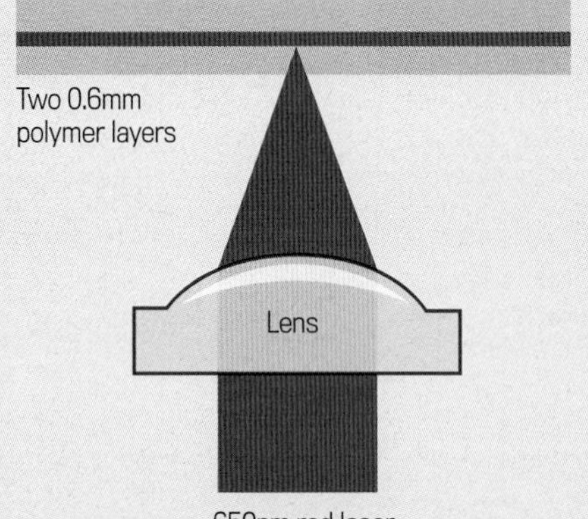

CAPACITY

4.7GB

Data on DVD can last up to 100 years

BLU-RAY

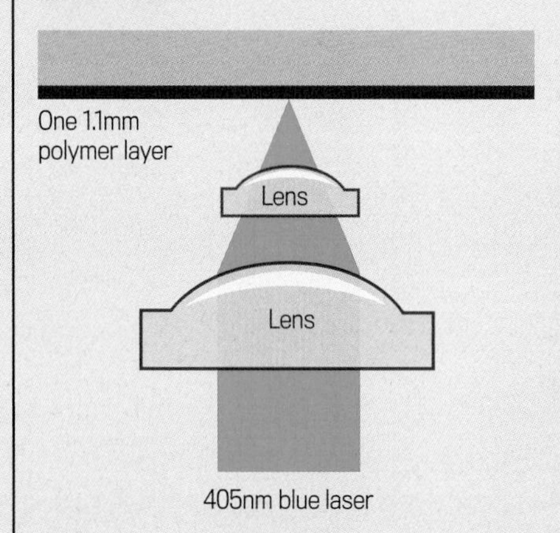

CAPACITY

25GB

Will Blu-ray be the last disc format?

STEVE SAYERS

COLOUR ELECTRONIC PAPER

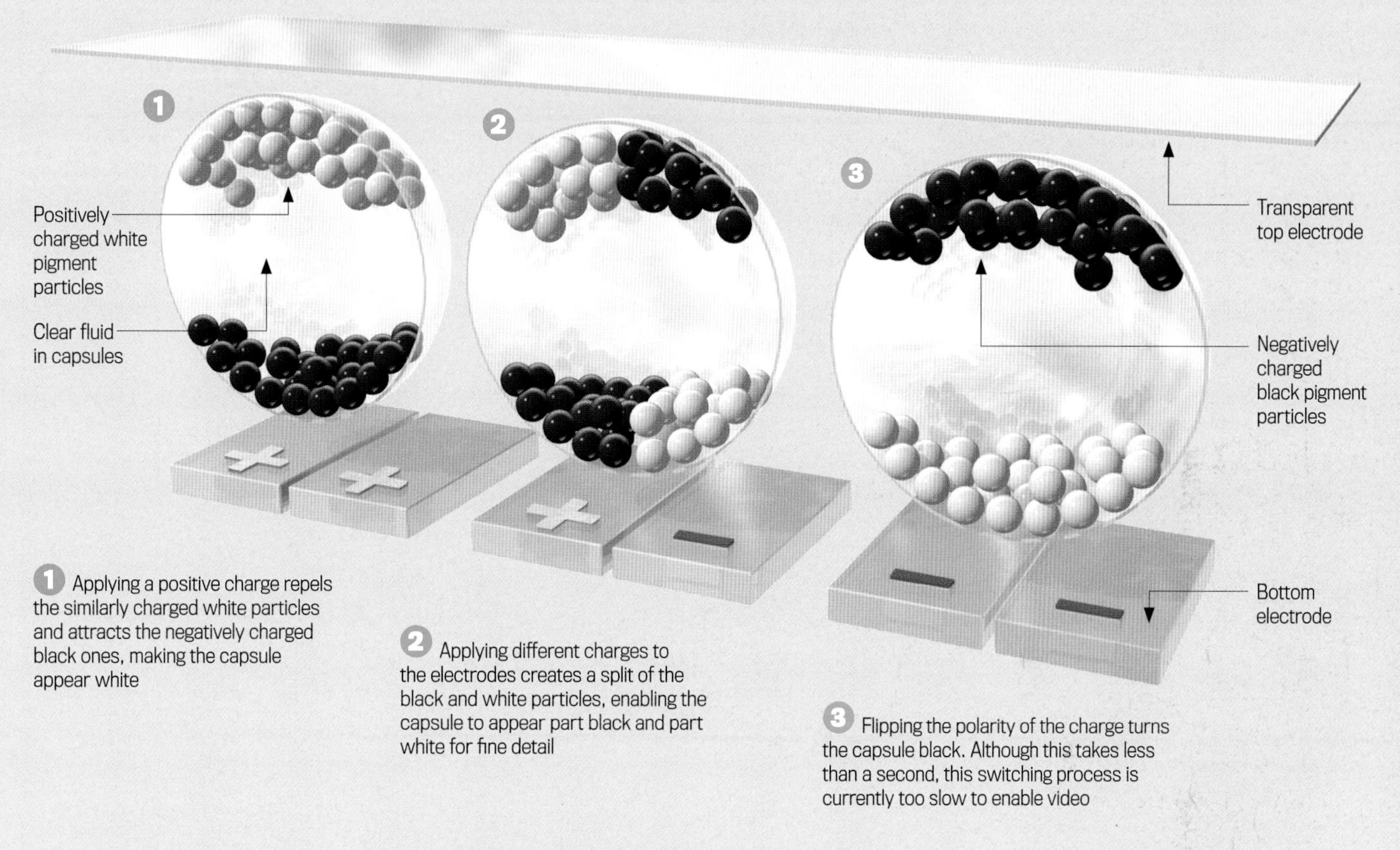

1 Applying a positive charge repels the similarly charged white particles and attracts the negatively charged black ones, making the capsule appear white

2 Applying different charges to the electrodes creates a split of the black and white particles, enabling the capsule to appear part black and part white for fine detail

3 Flipping the polarity of the charge turns the capsule black. Although this takes less than a second, this switching process is currently too slow to enable video

There's little not to love about electronic paper. It requires no backlight, can be viewed in the brightest sunlight, and the only time it uses power is when the on-screen image is changed, which means that battery life is measured in weeks instead of hours. The trouble is that e-readers like the Kindle and Kobo are monochrome.

However, a number of companies are working on colour displays. One, by Liquavista, attempts to do this by manipulating coloured liquids with electric fields. Another, by Xerox Fujifilm, manipulates cyan, magenta and yellow particles within a clear liquid.

Promising as these approaches are, by far the most advanced effort comes from the company E-Ink. Dubbed Triton (pictured, bottom right), this involves traditional monochrome pixels that reflect light. These are switched from black to white by adjusting the electric current passing through the screen, which alters the position of black and white pigment particles held in tiny capsules, as shown above. By placing a red, green and blue filter in front of the capsules, it creates subpixels that can make any colour except white. To create white, each pixel contains a region with no filter, allowing the monochrome display beneath to reflect light directly.

However, while this approach is straightforward, Triton's use of filters reduces the screen resolution by a factor of four. This is because what was previously the smallest visible unit (a monochrome pixel) becomes one of four blue, red, green or white sub-pixels.

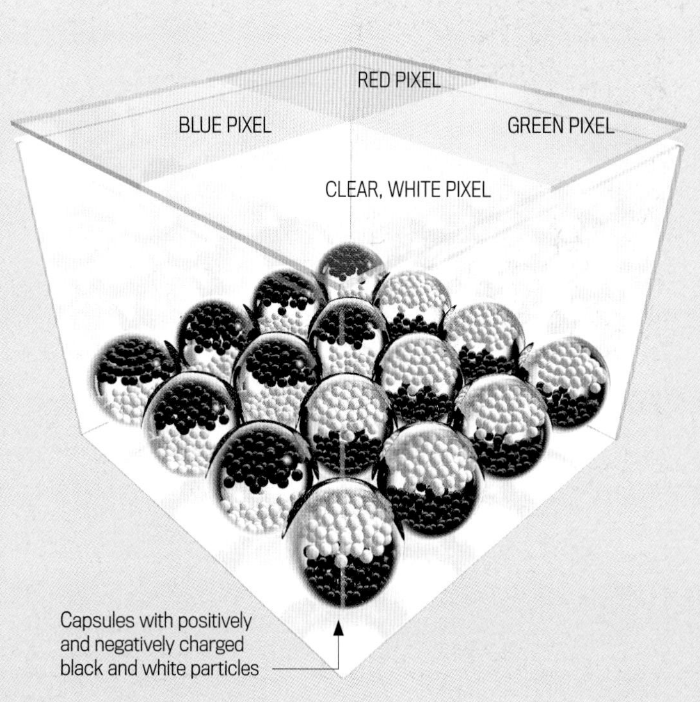

IAN NAYLOR

NEXT-GENERATION FINGERPRINTING

Every time you touch your fingertip to a surface, you imprint it with a precise pattern of sweat and oil. The odds of this fingerprint matching another individual's are one in 64 billion. Research into a new way of visualising fingerprints on metal surfaces could dramatically increase their use as an identification tool in criminal investigations.

Conventionally, collecting fingerprint forensic evidence involves dusting a coloured powder over the sticky residues left behind on a surface. But the poor sensitivity of this technique means that only 10 per cent of prints can be used as evidence in court. Researchers from the University of Leicester, the ISIS research centre in Oxford and France's Institut Laue-Langevin are developing a more sensitive approach. Known as a fluorescent fingerprint tag, it will identify prints on metal, like a knife or a bullet. An electric current is passed through the metal surface, allowing an 'electro-active' film to be applied over it. Any fingerprint residues on the surface are electrically insulating, so they act as a stencil and block the film from being deposited. This creates a negative image of the print on the bare metal.

The film is also electrochromic, meaning that it changes colour when an electrical voltage is applied. The research team, led by Professor Robert Hillman, also incorporated fluorophores into the film, molecules that change colour when exposed to light or ultra-violet rays.

Using electricity and light, the colouration can be finely tuned to create the best possible contrast between the fingerprint and the background surface.

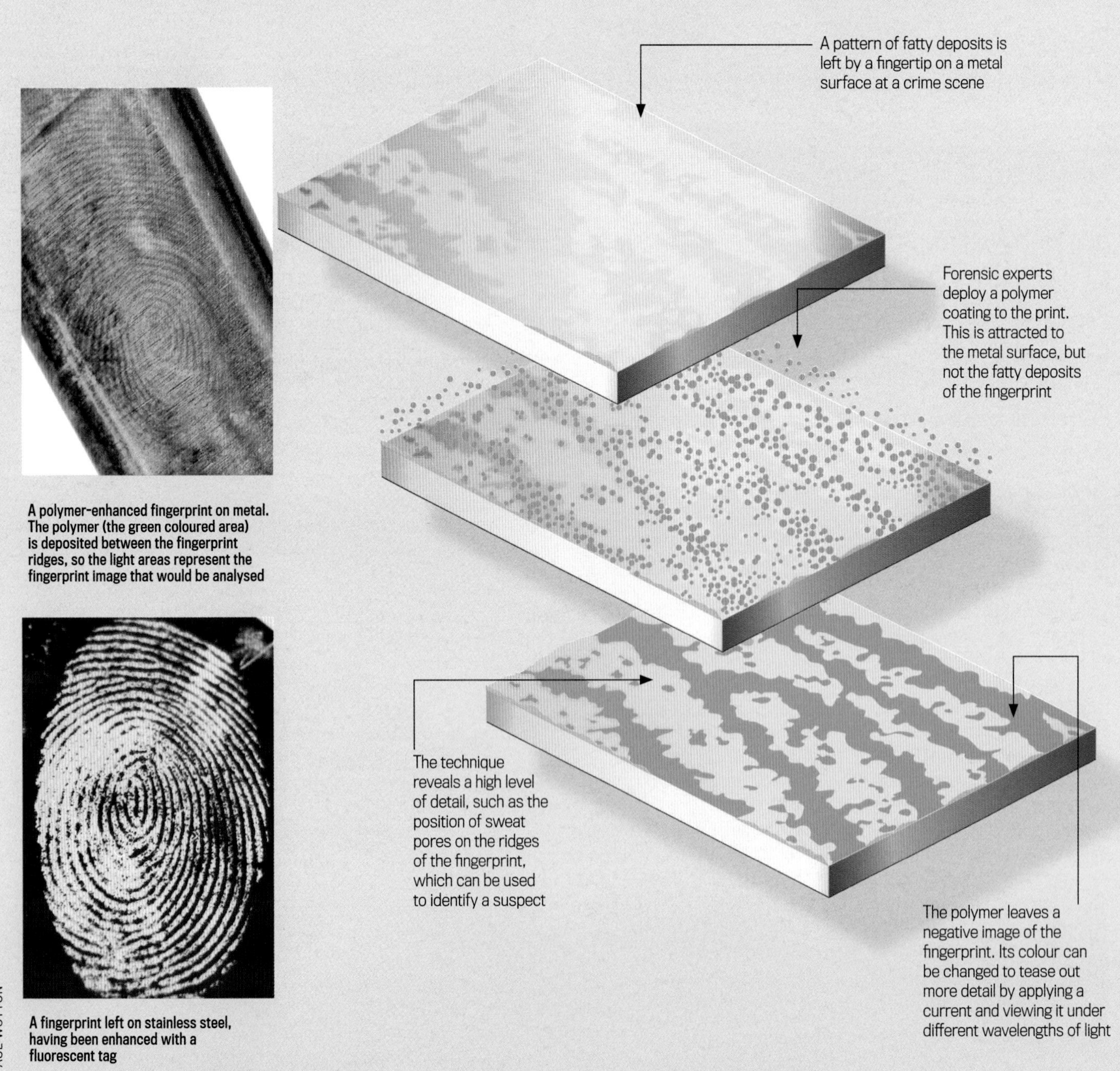

A polymer-enhanced fingerprint on metal. The polymer (the green coloured area) is deposited between the fingerprint ridges, so the light areas represent the fingerprint image that would be analysed

A fingerprint left on stainless steel, having been enhanced with a fluorescent tag

PAUL WOTTON

FRACKING

When Earth tremors were felt in Blackpool in 2011, the UK's only fracking site got the blame. Since then, the controversial technology has hardly left the news. Fracking, or hydraulic fracturing, is a method used to extract natural gas from rock found more than a kilometre underground. It takes over a month to drill a well deep enough to reach the gas-filled layer, known as shale. As it descends, the drill bit transmits information about its location to the surface. Once deep enough, it can be steered round to pass through the shale horizontally.

Water, sand and various chemicals are pumped at high pressure down the well and force fissures to form in the solid shale rock. Water flows into these cracks and the sand in the mixture holds them open. Once the water has been pumped back out, natural gas diffuses out of the cracks in the rock and up the well.

The UK is estimated to be sitting on enough shale gas to provide 25 years' worth of energy. Supporters argue it has the potential to lower energy prices and reduce coal consumption. But the risk of earthquakes, water pollution and methane leaks may keep it underground.

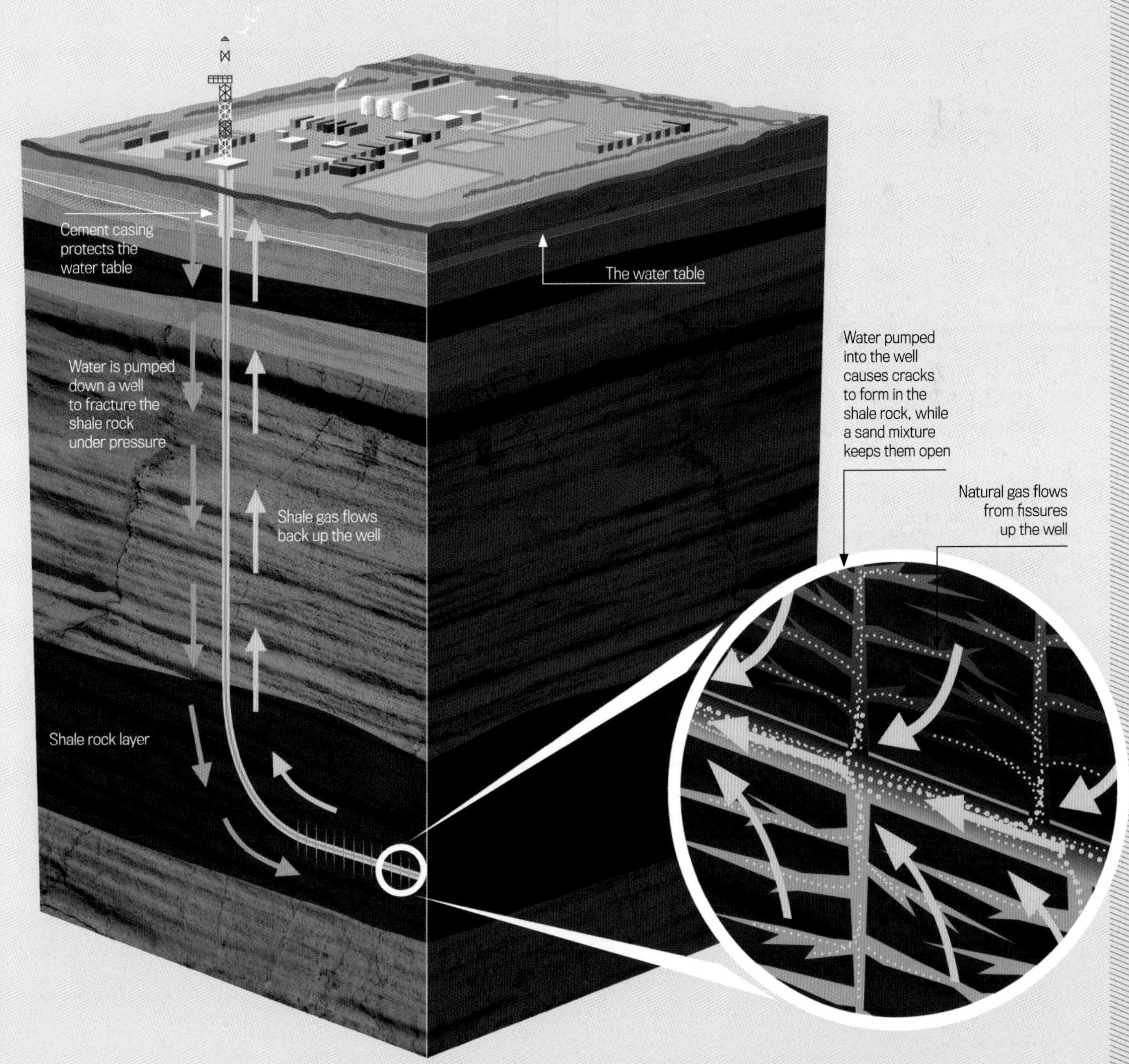

PAUL WESTON

SCANNING ELECTRON MICROSCOPE

Bacteria can appear like a swarm of menacing creatures and the surface of skin a rugged landscape – images from a scanning electron microscope deliver incredibly detailed views of very small things. By firing a beam of electrons at a target, scientists can observe smaller objects than it's possible to see with an optical microscope, which is limited by the wavelength of light. They have been used to study a wide range of materials and have helped scientists examine the structure of drugs to make them more effective.

ELECTRON GUN
Acting as an electron gun, a tungsten filament is heated, which emits negatively charged electrons

BEAM
The beam is typically 0.4 to 5nm in diameter – a nanometre is one-billionth of a metre

ANODE
A positively charged anode attracts the negatively charged electrons down the microscope. They pass through the middle of the anode as a beam

CONDENSER RINGS
Electromagnets known as condenser rings keep the beam focused, ensuring a maximum number of electrons hit the target

VACUUM
The whole apparatus is held in a vacuum to ensure the focused electron beam faces no interference from other particles

SCANNING COILS
These create a fluctuating magnetic field that's able to move the electron beam back and forth over the target

FOCUSING LENSES
A series of lenses focus the electron beam so that it is able to hit a tiny part of the sample

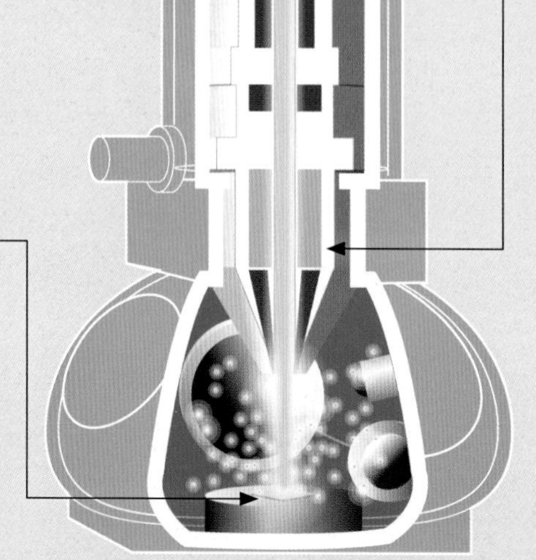

SAMPLE
When the electrons reach the sample chamber, they hit the target, knocking secondary atoms off it. A series of detectors pick up these secondary atoms and are able to discern the target's surface structure and composition. These include a CCD array that converts electrons striking a fluorescent plate into an image

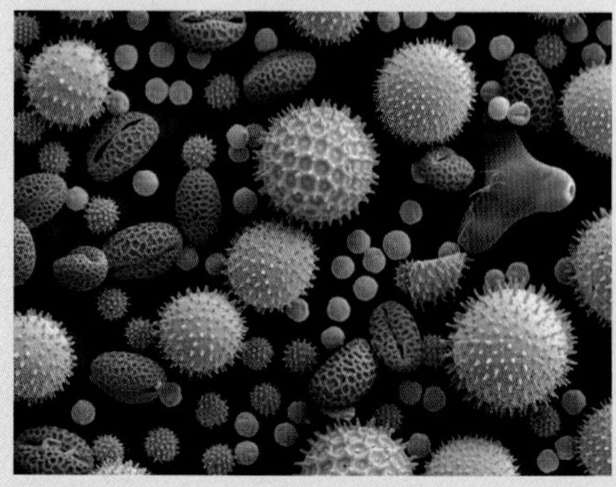

Placed under a scanning electron microscope, the intricate beauty of pollen grains is revealed

PAUL WESTON

THE ROAD-CHARGED ELECTRIC BUS

Electric buses that charge up as they drive along have been introduced in South Korea. A new fleet of electric buses in the city of Gumi make electric buses more efficient because they don't have to spend hours stationary and out of service.

The two buses, which run on an inner-city commuter route, receive power from underground coils built into the road. Developed at the Korea Advanced Institute of Science and Technology in Daejeon, this use of magnetic induction was introduced to the city in 2013.

As current flows through the underground coil, a magnetic field is created. This field then induces a corresponding field in a secondary coil, located on the bus. This allows power to be transferred between the two, charging the battery. It's the same technology that is used in wireless mobile phone charging mats.

The process is surprisingly efficient, so much so that only 5-15 per cent of the road along the bus's route would need the coils, helping to keep the cost of the system down. The buses receive 100kW of power while in motion, which is much more than can be delivered by a wireless charging station that you would use to charge a car in your garage – usually around 6.6kW.

By installing coils in areas that the buses typically linger, such as at traffic lights and bus stops, the vehicles can be charged even more efficiently.

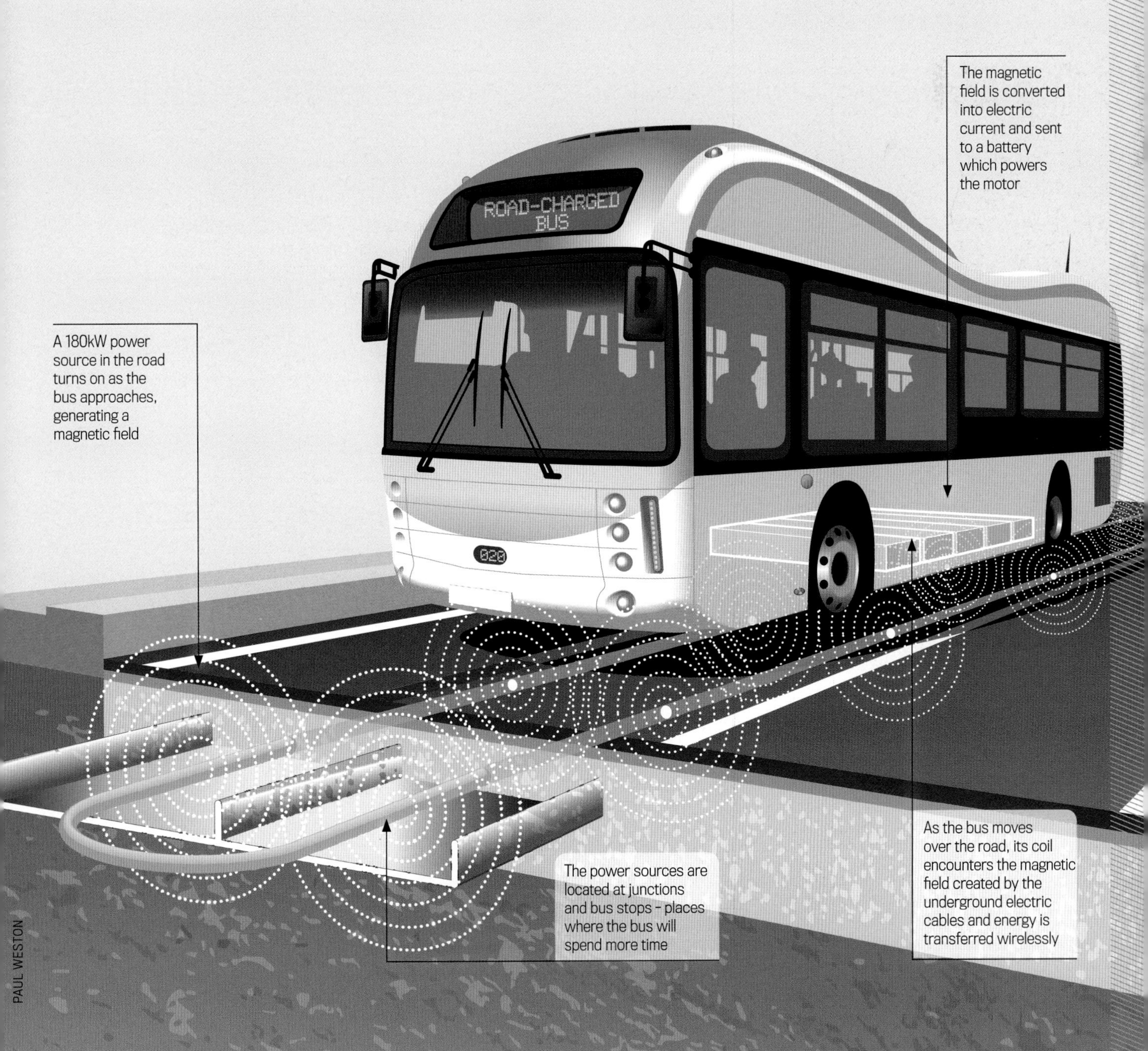

THE NANOPATCH

It's amazing to think that, while we now have the ability to print out body parts from a 3D printer, we still have to deliver medicines to our bodies by stabbing a needle into our flesh. It's painful. Enter the Nanopatch – a revolutionary vaccine-delivery system from medical technology start-up Vaxxas.

The Nanopatch is an array of about 20,000 tiny 'microprojections' that are able to fit onto a piece of silicon measuring just $1cm^2$. These microscopic pins are coated with a dry form of a vaccine. When the patch is applied, they penetrate just beneath the outer layer of the skin, the epidermis, which is rich in immune cells.

The high number of immune cells just beneath the skin enables the Nanopatch to be much more effective at creating an immune response than a needle injecting into muscle. It means that a much smaller amount of a vaccine, as little as 1/100th of a typical dose, can be used to the same effect. This is especially important in the developing world, where vaccines against diseases like malaria can prove costly.

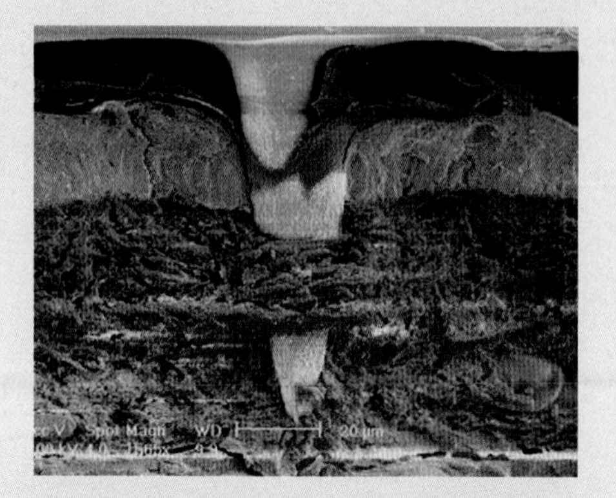

The 20,000 microprojections only pierce the top layer of skin, as can be seen in this magnified view

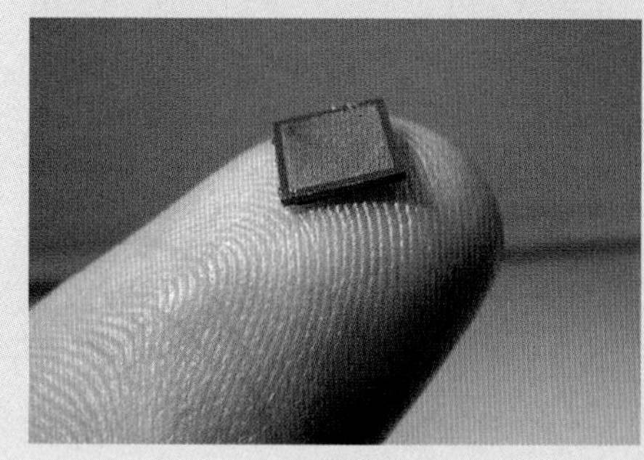

The Nanopatch is smaller than a postage stamp

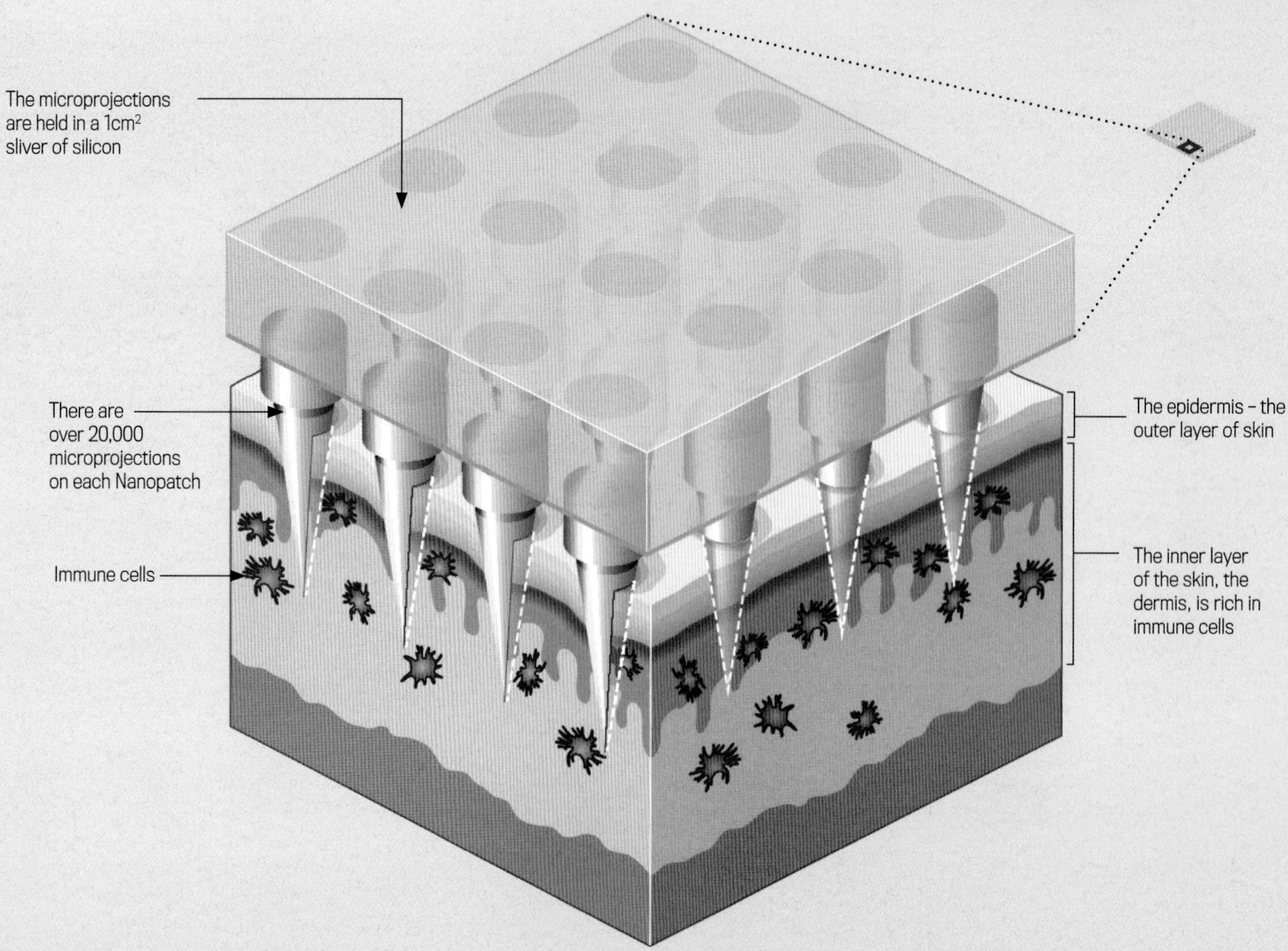

PAUL WESTON

THE SKYTRAN TRANSPORT SYSTEM

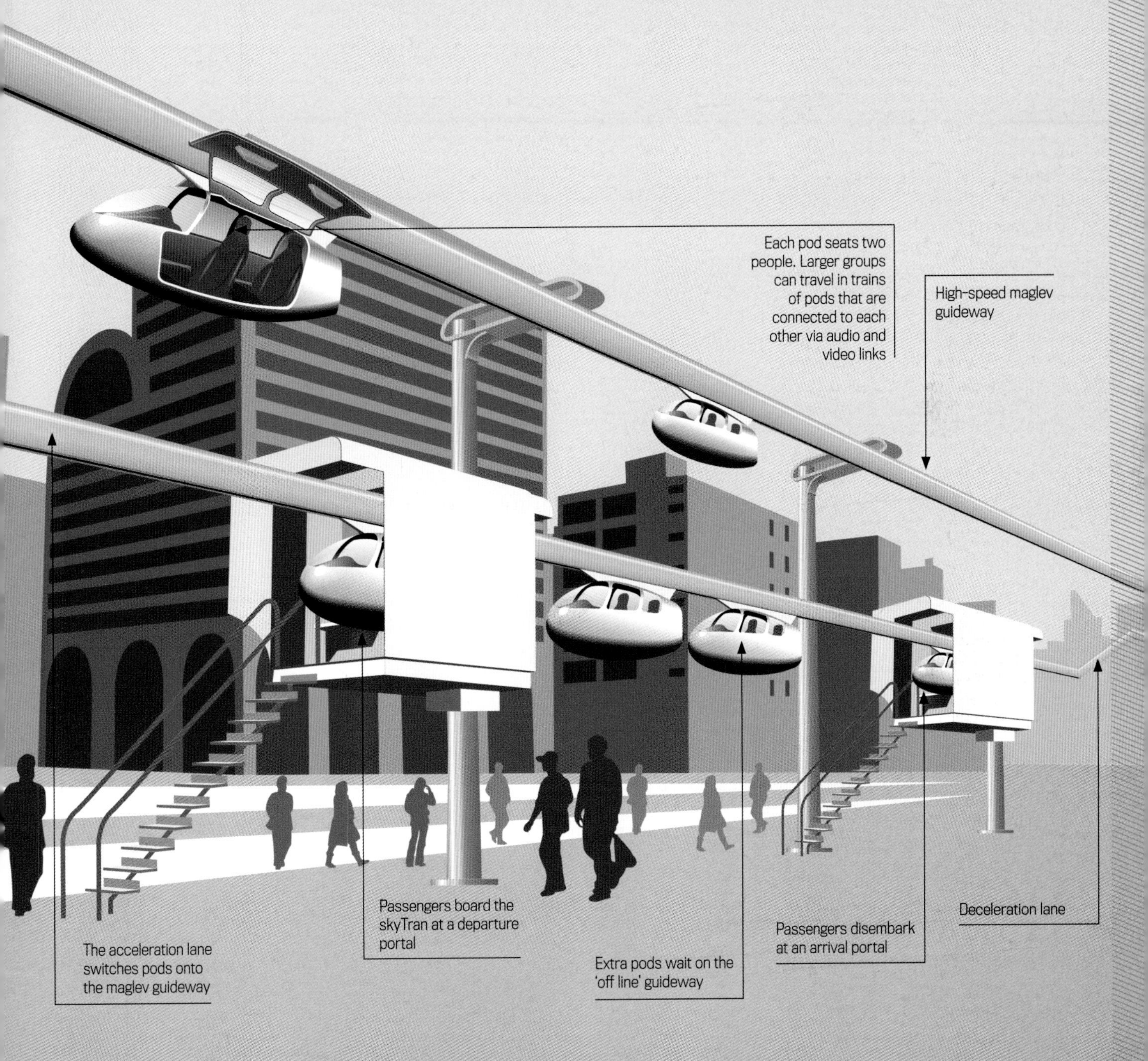

Travellers in Tel Aviv will soon be able to glide above the hustle and bustle of the city's congested roads in comfort. The magnetically levitating 'skyTran' is set to be built above the gridlocked city, with work aiming to be completed by the end of 2015. The system lets you board a personal cabin to take you around the city and, since it exploits the unused space above roads, it should be relatively cheap to build.

While the personal pods may look like they hang from the guideway, their connecting poles are actually being levitated within the supporting rail. Magnets are embedded in the top of the carriage's poles, which interact with an induction coil contained within the rail. The magnets induce a current in the coil when the pods move. This current produces its own magnetic field that repels the magnet in the pod, making it levitate. A separate electrified acceleration rail is needed at stops to initially get the pods moving - they can hit speeds of 240km/h (150mph). As the pods are relatively light, they don't need the powerful, energy intensive superconducting magnets used in maglev trains. It is even hoped the skyTran transport system can become energy self-sufficient by adding solar panels.

Since there is no contact between the pod and the rail, friction and noise is reduced, making for a more relaxing journey. What's more, the pods are summoned at the touch of a button when requested via the website or a mobile app.

PAUL WESTON

THE SCANNER PILL

Doctors may soon have an improved method to scan the oesophagus, which connects your throat and your stomach, for disease. A capsule the size of a multivitamin pill captures three-dimensional, cross-sectional images in greater detail than you get with traditional high-resolution endoscopy. In addition, it doesn't require patients to be sedated.

The pill contains a rotating laser tip that emits a beam of near-infrared light. Sensors in the pill record the light reflected back from the oesophageal lining. The transparent capsule is attached to a tether that connects to an imaging console, allowing a doctor to control it.

After a patient swallows the capsule, it's carried down the oesophagus by normal contraction of the surrounding muscles. When the capsule reaches the entrance to the stomach, it can be pulled back up.

The capsule has been used in trials at Massachusetts General Hospital in the US. It's hoped that it will eventually provide a cheap way of screening more people for cancer of the oesophagus.

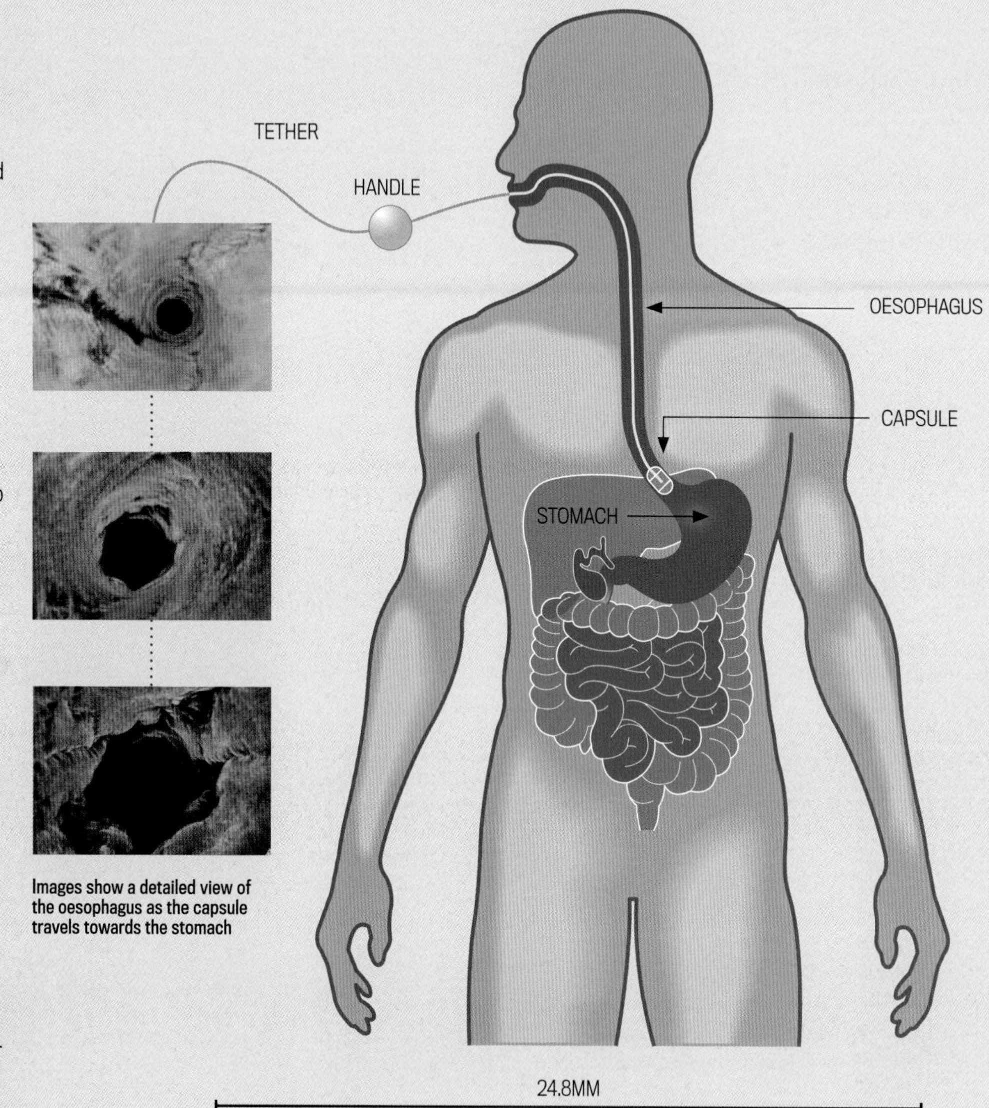

Images show a detailed view of the oesophagus as the capsule travels towards the stomach

INSIDE THE PILL

A beam of infrared light is sent down a fibre optic cable into a transparent capsule. The light is redirected and a driveshaft is rotated so that the beam spins in the pill. The reflected light is received by miniature optics and sent back up the fibre optic cable, where it's turned into an image.

PAUL WESTON

THE PILOTLESS PLANE

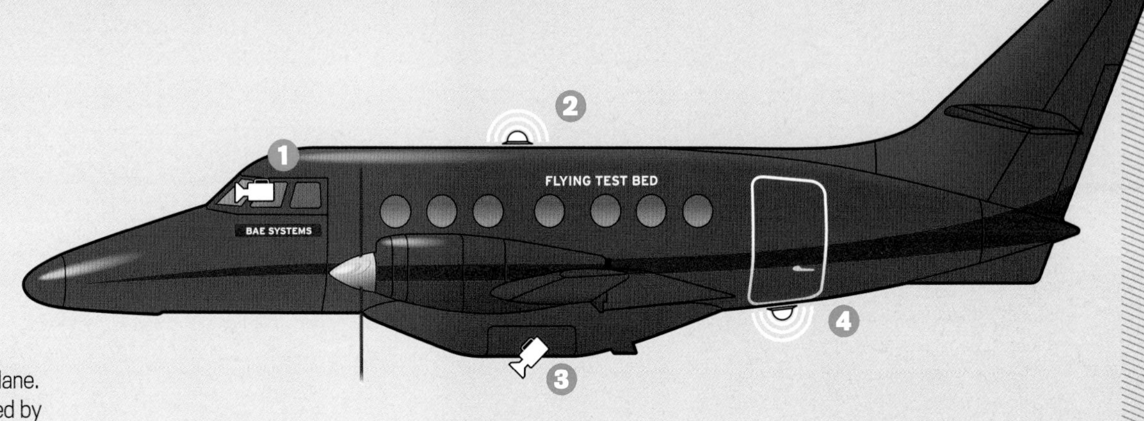

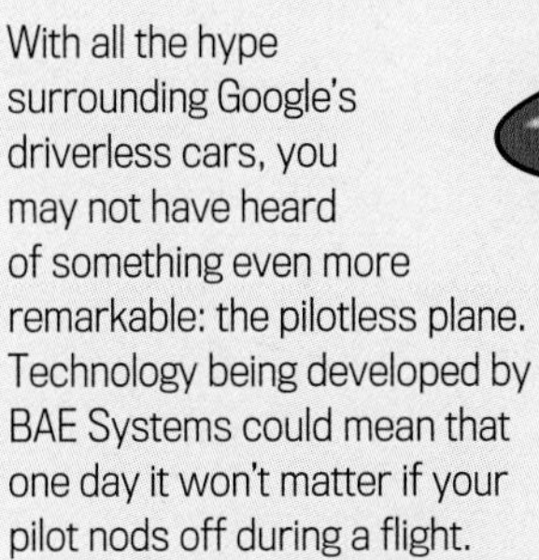

With all the hype surrounding Google's driverless cars, you may not have heard of something even more remarkable: the pilotless plane. Technology being developed by BAE Systems could mean that one day it won't matter if your pilot nods off during a flight.

The system needed to do this has been put through its paces over the Irish Sea. Integrated into a small passenger plane called (somewhat uninspiringly) 'The Flying Testbed', the technology, together with satellite communications, can do far more than your typical autopilot. While an autopilot can keep a plane on a level, accurate flight path and perform a landing, the new system is able to think for itself. The technology could be used in an emergency situation when the crew have been rendered unconscious, for instance. However, there are currently no plans to commercialise the system.

Using a camera mounted in the cockpit and a bank of computers in the tail, the aircraft can detect different cloud types before plotting evasive action if necessary – a world first. Similarly, the 'brain' of the plane has 'sense and avoid' technology, using its Aircraft Identification Antenna to pick up aircraft transponder signals. If it doesn't pick up a signal, the camera is used to make visual contact before the computer plots a safe course.

Finally, if you were to find yourself in the brace position, you're in safe hands. The aircraft is able to use an infrared camera mounted underneath, as well as its antenna, to detect a suitable landing site.

ANDREW BAKER

1 A cockpit-mounted camera detects potentially dangerous weather and nearby aircraft

2 The plane uses an antenna on the top for ground-based and satellite communications

3 An infrared camera can detect a suitable location to make an emergency landing

4 The Aircraft Identification Antenna enables the plane to avoid nearby aircraft

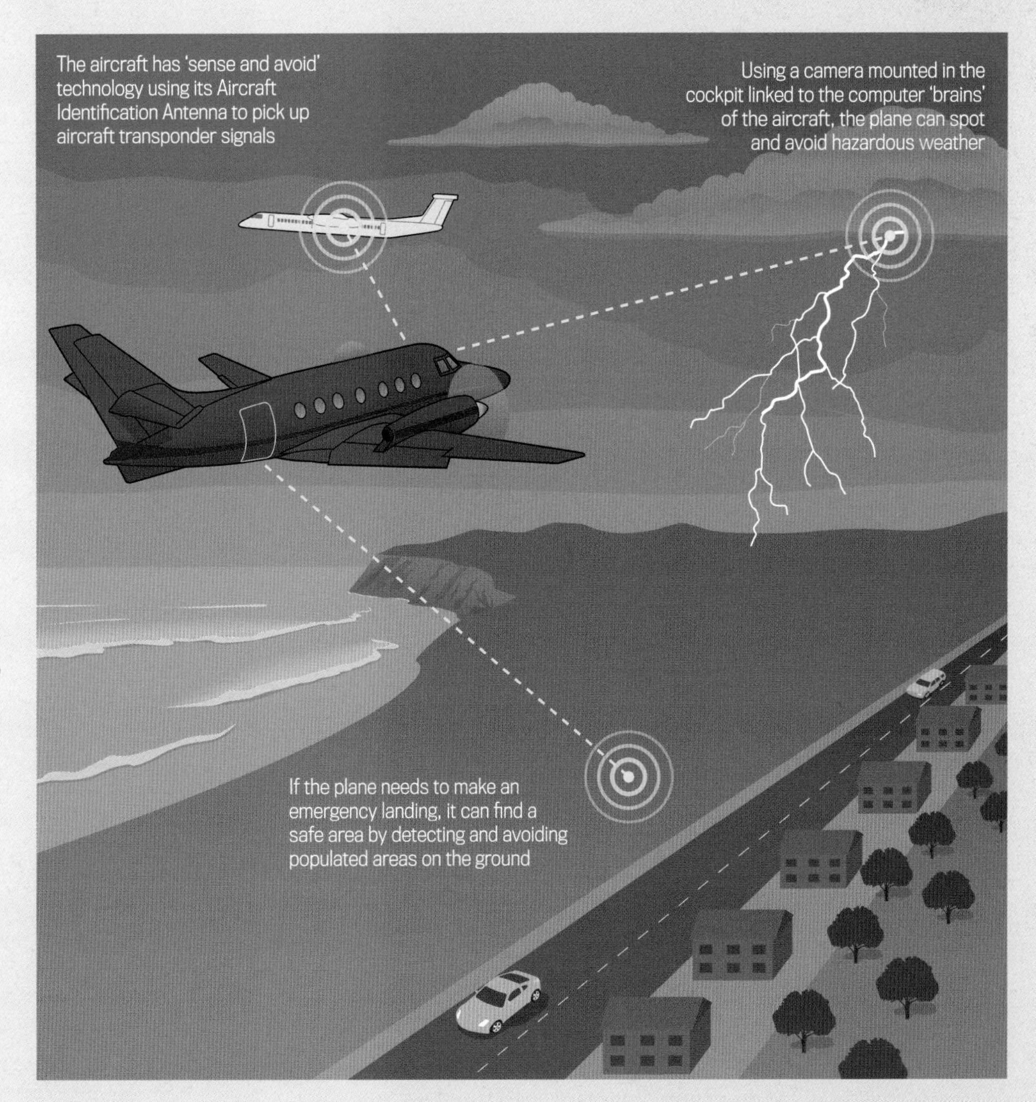

HEINZ-PETER BADER/REUTERS/CORBIS

Why is this ski jumper in a wind tunnel?

Gregor Schlierenzauer, a ski jumper with the Austrian World Cup team, is hanging from the ceiling of the Rail Tech Arsenal climatic wind tunnel in Vienna during a training session. The 100m (328ft) tunnel, the largest of its kind in the world, is normally used to test how buses and trains handle adverse conditions. It can produce any kind of weather, with winds of up to 300km/h (186mph), temperatures from -45°C to 60°C, simulated sunlight and controlled humidity.

In the tunnel, the athletes stay aloft for several minutes instead of the few seconds a jump lasts. They try different positions and improve their technique in real-time with their coach rather than analysing video footage afterwards. "You can change your style a bit, play with the air and maybe find the perfect position, which you could never do from a hill because the flight time is much, much shorter," says Florian Kotlaba, a team spokesperson.

For more great pictures, follow us on http://pinterest.com/sciencefocus

FOCUS SUBSCRIPTION ORDER FORM CODE: FOSBB14

☑ Yes, I would like to subscribe to BBC Focus Magazine and receive 3 issues for £3 by Direct Debit. After my trial, my subscription will continue at £17.85 for 6 issues – **saving 30%***

DIRECT Debit

Instruction to your bank or building society
Name and full postal address of your bank or building society:

Name of bank ______________________

Address ______________________

____

____

______________________ Postcode ______

Name(s) of account holder(s) ______________________

Branch sort code ☐☐☐☐☐☐

Bank/building society ac. no. ☐☐☐☐☐☐☐☐

Instruction to your bank/building society

Please pay Immediate Media Company Bristol Limited Debits from the account detailed in this instruction subject to the safeguards assured by the Direct Debit Guarantee. I understand that this instruction may remain with Immediate Media Company Bristol Limited and, if so, details will be passed electronically to my Bank/Building Society. ☐

Signature(s) ______________________

Date ______________________

Office use only

Originator's identification number: 7 1 0 6 4 4

Banks and building societies may not accept Direct Debit instructions for some types of account.

YOUR DETAILS (Essential)

Title ______ First name ______________ Surname ______________

Address ______________________

____

______________________ Postcode ______

Home tel number ______________________

Mobile tel number ______________________

Email address ______________________

Other payments for a year's subscription (13 issues)

☐ Europe – 13 issues by Credit/debit card or cheque for just £58.50

☐ ROW - 13 issues by Credit/debit card or cheque for just £63.00

☐ UK - 13 issues by credit/debit card or cheque (1 year) for £41.44 - **saving 25%**

CREDIT CARD

Visa ☐ Mastercard ☐ Maestro ☐

Card no. ☐☐☐☐ ☐☐☐☐ ☐☐☐☐ ☐☐☐☐

Issue no. (Maestro only) ☐☐ Valid from ☐☐ ☐☐ Expiry date ☐☐ ☐☐

Signature ______________________ **Date** ______

POST ORDER FORM TO:

FOCUS, FREEPOST LON16059, Sittingbourne, Kent, ME9 8DF

Your personal information will be used as set out in our Privacy Policy, which can be viewed at immediate.co.uk/privacy-policy.

Branded BBC titles are licensed from or published jointly with BBC Worldwide (the commercial arm of the BBC). Please tick here [ ] if you'd like to receive regular newsletters, special offers and promotions from BBC Worldwide by email. Your information will be handled in accordance with the BBC Worldwide privacy policy: http://www.bbcworldwide.com/privacy.aspx

*3 issues for £3 offer is only available to UK residents paying by Direct Debit. Your subscription will start with the next available issue. After you first 3 issues, your subscription will continue at £17.85 every 6 issues, saving you 30% on the shop price. If you cancel within two weeks of receiving your third issue, you will pay no more than £3. Offer ends 31st December 2015.

Offer ends 31 December 2015

EVERY MONTH, **FOCUS** BRINGS YOU...

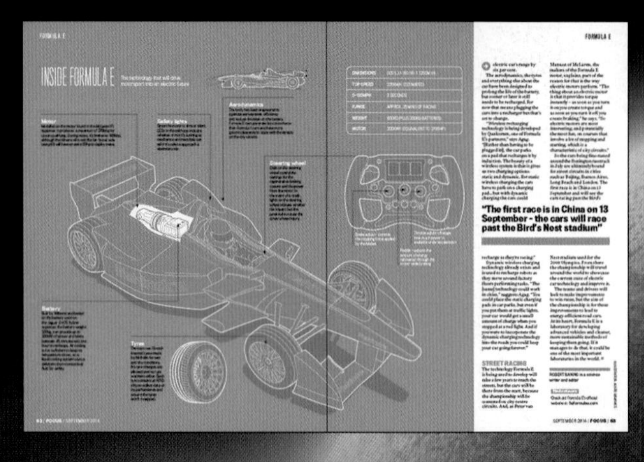

In-depth features: groundbreaking stories from the world of science, brought to you by top writers

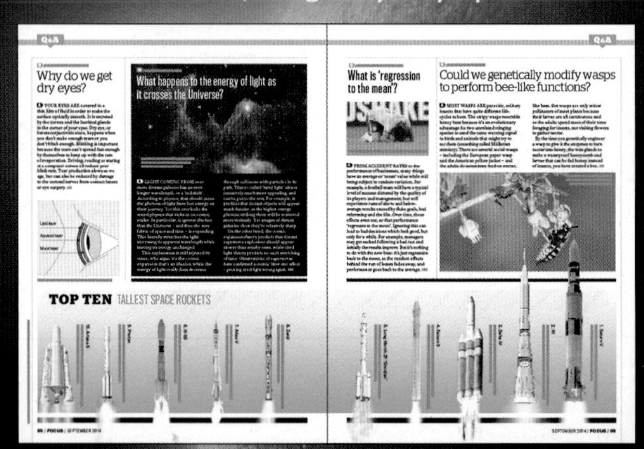

Q&A: do you have a burning question about the world around you? Our panel of experts have the answer

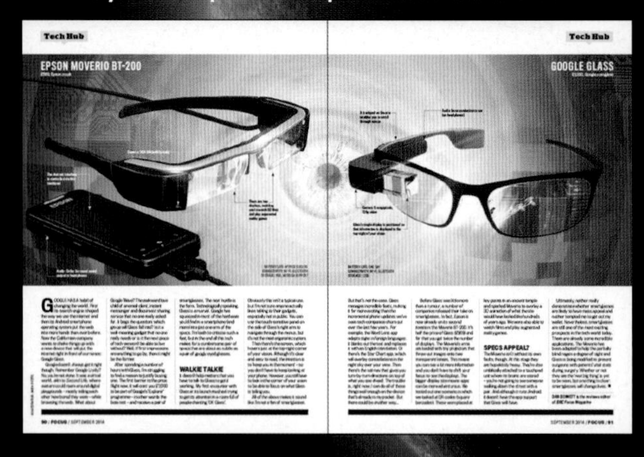

The latest gear: all the new technology you'll want to own is tried and tested by our team of reviewers

And much more...

SUBSCRIBE TODAY

GOOGLE